NELSON EDUCATION LTD

McMaster University

Discover

Psychology

Volume II

NELSON EDUCATION

NELSON EDUCATION

ISBN-13: 978-0-17-663809-2
ISBN-10: 0-17-663809-1

Layout and Design:
Science Media Lab (McMaster University)

The following chapters are based on copyright work in collaboration with several authors and have been modified to accompany the web lectures at McMaster University

Table of Contents

Developmental Psychology 5

Development...5

Research Methods with the Long View.............................6

1. Physiological Development....................................8

Conception: 8

Genetic Transmission:...8

Prenatal Development 10

Postnatal Development 10

2. Neural Development 13

Prenatal Development of the Nervous System......13

Post-natal Development of the Nervous System: Infancy and Childhood
....15

Experience-Expectant / Experience-Dependent....17

3. Cognitive Development..21

Cognitive Development: Infancy and Childhood....21

Beyond Piaget: Modern Perspective on Cognitive Development...........21

Cognitive Development: Adolescence....................22

Cognitive Development: Adulthood 23

Evolutionary Psychology 25

Introduction 25

What *is* Evolutionary Psychology...........................25

1. Essential Facts and Ideas About Evolution

The Concept of Evolution......................................28

The Theory of Evolution by Natural Selection........30

2. Why Evolutionary Theory Matters to Psychological Design.......33

Adaptations...33

Functionality...33

3. Mate Choice and Sexual Jealousy.................................... 36
    Sexual Selection.. 36
4. Kinship and Human Affairs.. 44
    Social Behaviour.. 44
    Genetic Relatedness... 46
5. Inclusive Fitness.. 48
    Inclusive Fitness & Behaviour.............................. 48
    Target Study: FAMILY HOMICIDE........................ 49
    Application Box: The Naturalistic Fallacy................... 53
    Kin Recognition.. 55
6. Parent-Offspring Conflict... 59
    Competition for Resources................................. 59
    An Evolutionary Arms Race................................ 62
Concluding Thoughts... 64
References..65
Neuroscience 70
1. Consciousness and awareness 72
    Epilepsy and the Split Brain................................72
2. Divisions of the Nervous System - The Central and Peripheral
Nervous Systems 73
    The Somatic and Autonomic Nervous Systems 74
3. The Nerve Cell and the Action Potential 74
    The Neuron..74
    Electrical Activity of the Neuron 77
    Communication Between Neurons 82
    Glial Cells 85
4. The Anatomy of the Nervous System 85
    Terminology 85
5. Studying the Brain.. 85
    Lesion Studies 86
    Electrical Stimulation and Single Cell recording 87
    Structural Neuroimaging 88
    Functional Neuroimaging...................................89

Draft

6. Brain Anatomy 91

    The Ventricles and the Cerebrospinal Fluid 91

    The Hindbrain 91

    The Midbrain 92

    The Forebrain 93

    The Cerebral Cortex 94

Sensory Systems 96

1. How Accurate are our Sensations and Perceptions? 97

2. The Inventing Brain 98

3. Introduction to Vision 101

4. The Stimulus 103

    Physical Characteristics of Light 103

5. The Eye 105

    Parts of the eye 105

    Visual Pathways 111

    Organization of Primary visual cortex 113

    Extra striate cortex 115

    Evolution of the Eye 116

6. Colour and Depth Perception 117

    Variations of Colour Vision 118

    Colour Mixing 118

    Theories of Colour Vision 118

    Colour Processing 121

    Colour Blindness 123

7. Depth, Distance & Motion 124

    Binocular cues to depth. 124

    Development of Depth Perception 126

    Evolution of Depth Perception 127

8. Vision & Eye Development 128

    Measuring infant visual acuity 128

9. Specialized Visual Systems 130

    Simple eye vs. compound eye 130

    Shape of pupil varies across species 130

Size of eyes across species. 130

Different photoreceptors in different species 131

10. Motion 131

Neural Pathways of Motion Perception 132

Motion Agnosia 132

11. Form Perception 133

Gestalt Principles of Grouping 133

Six principles of Gestalt organization 134

Role of expectation in perception of patterns and objects 138

Theories of object recognition in Humans 139

Recognition-by-components 139

Template Matching Model 140

Prototype Model 141

Perceptual Constancy 142

The 5 perceptual constancies 143

Development of Pattern, Object and Face Recognition 144

Object recognition 144

Size Constancy 144

Face Recognition 145

Visual Illusions 145

The Müller-Lyer illusion 146

The Ponzo illusion 147

The Matrix Problem 147

Developmental Psychology

Most research areas in psychology study behaviours *as they exist at a single point in time*. The questions involved generally concern how the characteristics and abilities of individuals interact with a particular situation to produce behaviour. Developmental psychologists. are interested in how individuals come to possess those characteristics and abilities. In order to answer these sorts of questions, it is necessary to take a wider perspective and look at how those characteristics change, develop, and are utilized over time.

Development

Many interesting psychological questions are inherently developmental in nature. Questions such as: How do the brain and nervous systems develop? How does the child develop the ability to interpret the world around her, and interact effectively with that world? How is language acquired? What are the causes of developmental disorders? In a very important way, developmental psychology is much like the other themes in psychology that we have explored in that it is not so much a 'separate sub-division' of psychology, but rather a particular perspective that has relevant things to say about almost all areas of psychology.

Before we proceed, we should clear up one popular misconception about developmental psychology. This branch of psychology is, in fact, concerned with the entire lifespan of human beings. Much of the research you will encounter will explore *childhood* development (although *adolescence* also gets a great deal of attention), but it is important to realize that there is no particular age at which developmental psychologists stop being interested. The developmental process starts at conception, and continues in one way or another until we die, and the entire scope of this process constitutes the subject matter of this area. The reason you will find so much research focused on childhood is that so many enormous and fundamental changes are concentrated in this period of our lives. We will

Draft

never stop changing and developing, but the speed, magnitude, and scope of change won't ever be as great as it is during our early years.

Research Methods with the Long View

Psychologists who study development may rely on the experimental method somewhat less often than other psychologists do, for several reasons. Critics of the experimental method within development point out that given the complexity of development, and the many factors that may affect development, it is difficult (perhaps impossible) to design an experiment in which all the potentially relevant extraneous variables have been controlled for. While we may only be interested in one aspect of development, such as the acquisition of language, in the 'real world' outside the laboratory this developmental process does not take place in a vacuum. Numerous other developmental processes are taking place at the same time in any individual, and trying to control for the effects that one process may have on another becomes difficult, if not impossible. And, even if we show through experimentation that some variable *can* influence development, it does not necessarily mean that it actually *does* influence normal development in the 'real world'. Moreover, critics point out that developmental change within a single system may be the product of the simultaneous action of a large number of variables: While there is no *theoretical* limit on the number of variables we might choose to manipulate in a single experiment, there are certainly practical limits (we probably can't afford to conduct experiments with hundreds of groups of subjects). As the *interaction* of these many variables may be more important than the effect of any one of them in isolation, the kind of experiment we could actually manage to conduct may not tell us very much about the normal course of development. Note, however, that your lectures will describe several cases where the experimental method has been successfully applied to the study of development, often through some rather ingenious innovations.

For the reasons cited above, the *quasi-experiment* is more commonly used as a research method in developmental psychology than in most other areas of psychology. This is a method of dealing with the fact that we frequently can't manipulate a variable of interest, such as age or gender. Therefore, instead of making a futile attempt to randomly assign subjects to different levels of that variable, we simply group our subjects based on their *existing* level of that variable. This is simple enough to do; we can easily sort all the three-year-olds into one group and the four-year-olds into another, etc… Note however that when we do this, we are not randomly assigning subjects to conditions, and therefore cannot make the same kind of 'cause and effect' interpretations of our data that a true experiment would allow. For much the same reason, you will find correlational techniques are also frequently used in the study of development. In such studies, we again take the world as we find it, rather than attempting to manipulate the variables of interest.

There are two basic kinds of questions that can be asked about development: *Descriptive* or *normative* research asks questions about how things normally change from age to age. What should we expect to see in the course of an individual's development? What is the individual capable of at any given age? *Analytic* research asks about the processes and variables that are responsible for the changes in abilities and needs from age to age. Why does change occur? In both cases the passage of time is an important variable.

There are two general types of research design we might use if one of our critical variables is the age of individuals. One of these is the *longitudinal* design. In this design, we compare development at different ages by following the same group of individuals over a period of time, and repeatedly describing or testing those individuals - a form of *within-subjects* design. There are both advantages and disadvantages to the longitudinal design.

The primary advantage of the longitudinal approach is that, by observing the same individuals over time, we can eliminate a lot of potential extraneous variables (EVs). When we compare our subjects to *themselves* at different points in time, we don't have to worry about our results being influenced by any pre-existing differences *between* people. As obvious and logical as it may seem, the longitudinal design also has several disadvantages. One is that longitudinal studies can be very time-consuming and costly if they follow individuals for a number of years. Some famous long-term studies (including several that are still going on) have run for more than 20 years, involving several generations of researchers.

Another disadvantage of longitudinal studies is that subjects may be lost over time due to death, moving away, or simply the refusal to continue participating. These risks increase with the length of the study. In addition, if subjects are given the same tests repeatedly over the course of a longitudinal study, their performance may change simply as a result of practice. Finally, in some cases (e.g. social or emotional development) the developmental changes we observe in a longitudinal study may reflect experiences specific to subjects of a particular *cohort* (i.e., a group of people born at the same time in the same society) rather than reflecting universal developmental trends. We call this a *cohort effect*. Consider a typical multi-generational family: The grandparents were born in the 1930s during the Great Depression. The parents were born in the 1950s, when economic prosperity and steady employment were the norm. The children were born in the 1970s, by which time the great economic boom of the 50's was over and mass media began to have profound effects on public attitudes. In many ways, these people may have more in common with others of their generation than their ancestors and descendants. Development may be profoundly affected in a number of ways by social and economic conditions. Each cohort was exposed to a very different set of these conditions. These unique experiences may have shaped their social and personality development in ways that do not apply to individuals born at other times.

If developmental psychology is interested in the study of how humans develop from conception through death and all of the milestones in between, what has been found? The rest of this chapter is organized into 3 sections that summarize these findings: physiological, neural, and cognitive.

Physiological Development

Conception:

In the beginning, there was a sperm and an egg. Well actually there were about 200 million sperm and 1 egg. Out of the millions of sperm on this mission – only one will prevail. So begins the epic journey of conception.

While a woman is born with all of the immature eggs she will ever have, men begin producing sperm cells at puberty. That one, single egg has been waiting the woman's whole life to mature and be released – while those millions of sperm are relatively new, produced sometime in the past few days or weeks. Upon release, those sperm race towards what they hope is a mature egg. The few sperm that get to approach the egg – a cell about 85,000 times their size – release a digestive enzyme that eats away at the egg's protective coating allowing the sperm to penetrate. As soon as one sperm begins to penetrate, the egg's surface blocks out all others from entering, and sends out projections to pull the sperm in. After 12 hours or so, the egg's nucleus and sperm's nucleus fuse – creating your unique genetic blueprint.

Genetic Transmission:

Your genetic blueprint is made up of 23 pairs of **chromosomes**, half donated from your father and half from your mother. Chromosomes are made up of a long coil of **DNA** *(deoxyribonucleic acid),* which contains the biochemical units of heredity, which are **genes.** Genes are segments of the DNA molecule that are capable of synthesizing proteins, the building blocks of our physical development. The complete set of instructions for an organism is called a **genome.** The human genome consists of 30,000 or so genes, a complete set of which is contained in every single cell in your body. Think of all the genetic information we are constantly leaving behind.

Dominant and Recessive Genes. Like chromosomes, genes come in pairs, with one member of each pair donated by each parent. The two genes in each pair may or may not be identical. For example, if both genes in a pair specify the same eye color (e.g., both coding for brown), then that baby will have brown eyes. If the genes in the pair are different, then you have a more complicated story. In humans, the genes that code for brown eyes are **dominant**, meaning they will exert their effect regardless of what the other member of the gene pair codes for. The gene for blue eyes is **recessive**, which will lead to blue eyes only if the other member of the gene pair also codes for blue. In other words, a dominant trait (e.g., brown eyes, dark hair, dimples) will be expressed if either parent contributes the genetic instructions for it, while a recessive trait (e.g., blue eyes, baldness and red hair) will only be expressed if both parents contribute a genetic instruction for it. While a single gene pair governs many human traits, most of an organism's attributes are governed by many gene pairs, a pattern know as **polygenic inheritance**. Thus different gene pairs may control different aspects of a particular trait, or at different stages of a trait's development.

It is important to note that genes do not directly determine observable traits. Rather, each gene controls the production of a particular protein or enzyme that in turn regulates a biochemical sequence within the developing organism, determining the traits that get expressed. Therefore, the link between your **genotype** (genetic blueprint) and your **phenotype** (observable traits) is indirect. Genes guide the biochemical processes that lead to your observable traits, but so do many other factors. While it is true that some traits appear to be more genetically heritable than others, no characteristic is entirely determined by genes.

Sex Determination. Biological sex is one trait strongly governed by genes. The master gene model of sex determination suggests that the SRY gene, located on the 23rd chromosome, is responsible for determining the sex of an individual. Females have two X chromosomes (**XX**), and contribute an X chromosome to their offspring. Males have an X and a Y chromosome (**XY**), and can contribute either. Thus, sex determination (XX or XY) in humans is entirely dependent upon the genetic contribution of the males. A more recent and empirically adequate model is the cascade gene model that suggests the SRY gene is only one gene amongst many interacting genes that produce the sex of an individual, and that both female and male factors contribute.

A number of additional influences contribute to a human's sex phenotype. For example, in the case of **androgen insensitivity syndrome**, individuals are biologically male, but are resistant to the male hormones (androgens) that influence the development of male sex characteristics. Thus, an individual with androgen insensitivity syndrome may have some or all of the outward physical characteristics of a female, but has male reproductive organs. As well, because sex determination is more complex than once thought, the strict dichotomy that we categorize sex by is somewhat arbitrary. The high prevalence of sexually ambiguous individuals suggests that sex exists more so along a continuum, and this strict separation is in part the result of socially imposed norms.

Prenatal Development

Determining your genotype is a relatively easy process considering what comes next. Once the egg is fertilized, the resulting zygote enters a period of rapid cell division. Less than half of all fertilized eggs survive beyond the first two weeks of conception (Grobstein, 1970; Hall, 2004). Approximately ten days after conception, the zygote attaches to the uterine wall via the placenta, a source of nourishment for the rapidly developing cell mass, now recognized as an **embryo**. At this point, the embryo is made up of undifferentiated or unspecialized **embryonic stem cells.** Soon after attaching to the uterine wall, the cells begin to differentiate, specializing in structure and function. Some become brain cells, others go on to produce the vital organs, and so on.

After approximately 6 weeks of gestation, the embryo has primordial gonads that are not yet sexually differentiated. A week or so later, fetuses with an XY chromosome develop testes from these primordial gonads, which produce **androgens** (male hormones) that guide the development of the external male genitalia and male sexual organs. For an XX fetus, ovarian development factors work to produce **estrogens** (female hormones) that guide the development of external female genitalia and female sexual organs. As was commonly thought before, sex differentiation is not solely determined by active male factors; the female is not the default, passive pathway.

By two months after conception, the mass of cells has grown to about one inch in length and is now called a **fetus**, Latin for "offspring" or "young one". In the next month, the fetus grows to about 3 inches in length and begins to look "human", with some functioning organ systems and a number of early reflexes. By 7 months after conception, the fetus has grown to about 16 inches in length, has a fully developed reflex pattern, can cry, breathe, and swallow, and has a good chance of surviving in the harsh extra-uterine environment or the 'outside world'.

Postnatal Development

MOTOR DEVELOPMENT: INFANCY & CHILDHOOD

A human infant is born with very few motor skills, but is endowed with an array of instincts and reflexes designed to aid in survival and development outside of the womb. While a newborn cannot reach for an object, if one comes in contact with her hand, she will grasp it tightly. When her cheek is stroked, she will turn toward the touch. Mouth agape, she will close in on whatever she finds, and suck, a behavior known as the **rooting reflex.** Within weeks of birth, though an infant is unable to point to her mother, she will orient her head towards her voice (Mills & Melhuish, 1974).

The majority of individuals develop according to an orderly sequence of genetically determined biological growth processes; this period of development is known generally as **maturation.** Maturation determines many of our gross commonalities e.g., babies coo before they babble, although individual differences and experiences adjust the basic course of maturation e.g. the exact age at which each baby starts babbling.

As an infant matures, more complex motor skills develop. Many of the early reflexes disappear and are replaced by purposeful behaviors. For example, babies stop reflexively grasping around 3-4 months of age, but begin to voluntarily grasp around 5 months of age, and can grasp small objects with their thumbs and forefingers by 12 months of age. Although there are individual differences in timing, the sequence of most motor skills is universal. Babies roll over before they can sit unsupported, and they crawl on all fours before they can walk. About 90% of babies can walk by the time they are 15 months old (Frankenburg et al., 1992).

Once a baby masters the gross motor movements of locomotion, he can focus on more fine motor skills. By the second year of life, a toddler can pull, push, and dump objects. Not only that, he can pull off hats and socks, turn pages in a book, scribble with crayons, stack a small tower of blocks, feed himself with a spoon (albeit, messily), toss or roll a ball, open cabinets and drawers, and walk backwards. With all of these motor skills, and little understanding of the dangers of the world, this is an exceptional time for toddlers to explore and manipulate their environment, and likely get into some trouble along the way.

Between the ages of 3 and 4, a child has developed many of the motor skills necessary to play with fully developed children. Among other skills, children in this age group have the ability to toss a ball overhead and possibly catch it, kick a ball forward, walk in a straight line, jump with both feet, build a giant tower of blocks, feed herself almost entirely on her own, and walk up and down stairs without support. By age 5, she is hopping and jumping, climbing, using a fork and spoon, dressing herself without assistance, doing somersaults, and standing on one foot for 10 seconds or longer. By middle childhood, most children are as coordinated as adults and continue to work on their most important task: physical growth.

PHYSIOLOGICAL DEVELOPMENT IN ADOLESCENCE

Physical growth is not the only important physiological development; the body must also begin preparing itself for sexual maturity and eventual adulthood. **Adolescence** begins with the onset of **puberty**, the period of sexual maturation during which a person can become capable of reproduction. Most of us may fondly, or not so fondly, recall the days of elementary school health class where we were told to expect major changes in our bodies: hair in unusual places, a redistribution of body fat, pimples, sexual attraction, and a lifetime's worth of awkward moments.

Puberty marks the second major hormonally driven set of physical changes in the human body (the first being in-utero). Like all endocrine functions, puberty starts with commands sent from the hypothalamus to the pituitary gland. The pituitary gland releases **gonadotrophic hormones,** from the Greek *gonos* meaning "reproduction" and *trop* meaning, "Influence on". Gonadotrophic hormones influence reproduction by stimulating dramatic growth and maturation of the reproductive organs and external genitalia. In males, the onset of puberty is marked by an increased output of **testosterone**, leading to the enlargement of the testes and penis, lengthening of the vocal chords, an increase in body hair, and the ability to ejaculate. In females, **estrogen** is released by the ovaries, stimulating the growth of breasts, widening of the hips, growth of pubic and underarm hair, and the beginning of menstruation or **menarche.**

PHYSIOLOGICAL DEVELOPMENT IN MIDDLE ADULTHOOD

Once the physical awkwardness of adolescence fades, we begin to come into our own as young adults. Our physical abilities generally peak in our mid-twenties; however, this peak is followed by decline. The decline of abilities such as reaction time, muscular strength, and cardiac output happens gradually over time. However, a person's physical abilities can continue to peak if they are continuously used; the 60 year-old marathon runner is in better physical condition than the 25 year-old couch potato.

Aging also leads to a decline in fertility, due mainly to decreases in the production of sex hormones. In women, the decline is far more rapid than in men, with the likelihood of pregnancy decreasing after the age of 35 and dropping off when menstruation ceases at **menopause**, typically around age 50. While men do not experience a clear equivalent to menopause, they do not get to age without a hitch. Men do experience a gradual decline in sperm count, speed of ejaculation, and erection strength. Due to a decrease in testosterone in both sexes, libido also often decreases with age.

PHYSIOLOGICAL DEVELOPMENT IN OLDER ADULTHOOD

Why do we age? From an evolutionary perspective, we are designed to survive long enough to pass on our genes through reproduction and engage in child-rearing. However, we have increased our life expectancy dramatically in the past 50 years. Worldwide, we now live an average of 21 years longer than we did in 1955, with the current life expectancy at birth 68 years old and over 80 in some countries of the Global North. Essentially, we are living well past our age of reproductive utility, and into an age past our ability to contribute resources, putting the burden of our care on our offspring.

A number of physical abilities decline in older adulthood, including the amount of physical activity and the intensity of physical activity that can be tolerated. Another physical ability that declines is the ability to fight off life-threatening diseases. Age-related decline in immune function or **immunosenescence** occurs. However, the accumulation of a lifetime of antibodies also means that older adults are less likely to contract short-term ailments such as the common cold. Although there is no way to stop the aging process, it is possible to fight the ravages of aging with physical activity. Moderate exercise has been shown to increase immune function (Nieman, 2008), protection from chronic diseases (DiPietro, 2001), and reaction speed while driving (Marmeliera, 2011), while decreasing general chances of mortality (Talbot et al., 2007).

Neural Development

Prenatal Development of the Nervous System

The fact that every individual begins as a mass of undifferentiated cells is nothing short of amazing. Some of those cells are destined to become the nervous system, endowed with the capability to perceive the world, and react to saliency in the environment. The nervous system starts developing about 3 weeks after conception with the formation of primitive neural tissue, known as the **neural plate**. The neural plate folds and closes to become the **neural tube**, that then leads to the development of the brain and spinal cord. The neural tube is lined with neural stem cells that give rise to all cells of the nervous system. The basic human brain regions of the forebrain, midbrain, and hindbrain are visible by about 28 days. While the brain begins to look distinctly human by 100 days after conception, it does not form the sulci and gyri that are characteristic of the adult mammalian brain until about 7 months.

EFFECT OF PRENATAL ENVIRONMENT

Nutrition

Since the neural tube is the basis for the future nervous system, proper formation is critical for typical development. **Neural tube defects** are among the most common types of birth defects, with effects ranging from devastating to fatal. For example, if the tube fails to seal in the head end of the embryo, this results in *anencephaly*, the failure to develop the cerebral cortex, and is always fatal. If the tube fails to seal at its lower end, this results in *spina bifida*, where part of the spinal cord may develop outside of the spine. Spina bifida ranges in severity, from symptomless to highly disabling, with issues such as paralysis and sensory loss. The incidence of neural tube defects can be greatly reduced if the mother consumes folic acid prior to conception. Folic acid is a B vitamin found in large amounts in leafy vegetables, legumes, liver, and sunflower seeds.

Teratogens

Teratogens can come in all forms, and have a broad variety of effects, including neural tube defects. Teratogens can have an effect at any point during pregnancy, but in general, the earlier a fetus is exposed to teratogenic agents, the more harm can be done due to increased vulnerability in early pregnancy. A teratogen that causes damage to the nervous system at an early stage in fetal development is likely to influence the remainder of neural development.

One of the most common of all teratogens is alcohol. When a pregnant woman consumes alcohol it enters her fetal blood supply. If a woman drinks heavily, this may result in birth defects such as **Fetal Alcohol Syndrome (FAS).** FAS results in structural and functional abnormalities of the nervous system, and is widely considered to be the leading cause of developmental delay (e.g., Abel & Sokol, 1986; 1987; Nichols, 1994). Although it is true that even one incidence of binge drinking can lead to FAS, light to moderate drinking during pregnancy does not seem to increase the incidence of FAS (e.g., Kelly et al., 2009; Day, 1992; Abel, 1996; Polygenis et al., 1998). Further, until the embryo shares its mother's blood supply, about 10 days after conception, it is fairly safe against alcohol's effects.

While it is fairly easy to avoid alcohol and industrial chemicals during pregnancy, some teratogens are a bit less obvious in their approach. There is evidence that contracting the flu during pregnancy may increase the risk that the baby will develop schizophrenia as an adult (Watson et al., 1999). In addition, severe maternal stress (such as living through a serious earthquake) during pregnancy may increase the risk of the baby developing depression as an adult (Watson et al., 1999). Thus, an influenza infection or severe stress during pregnancy may act as teratogens, disrupting the development of the fetal brain and increasing the risk of psychopathology.

Sensory Experience

Although the womb is a dark space with a constant temperature, it is by no means devoid of sensory experience. The sensations experienced by the fetus drive the early development of complex sensory systems. Babies are born with sensory systems that are more or less ready to perceive in a world teeming with sensory information.

Vision is often considered to be the primary sense in mature and sighted humans. At birth, the visual system is relatively immature. The womb is an environment quite devoid of visual information, but the foundations for a complex visual system develop nonetheless. Prior to receiving any visual information, neural pathways in the developing visual system are restructured and highly organized. This seems to occur largely because of **spontaneous patterned activity** in the retina that helps to strengthen and organize the connectivity of the visual system (e.g., Wong, 1999). This spontaneous activity seems to prepare the brain for the visual world by mimicking the basic patterns of input that the system can expect to see when individuals first open their eyes.

Audition, on the other hand, is fairly mature at birth: primary auditory components such as the cochlea have developed to near adult levels (Moore & Linthicum, 2007). Between the sounds of the blood flowing through the placenta, the mother's heartbeat and other body functions, as well as her voice reverberating through her body, the womb is actually quite a loud place. At times, the uterine environment can be as loud as 80 decibels (Gerhardt & Abrams, 1996) – as loud as a crowded dance floor on a Saturday night. The uterine auditory environment is memorable to the point that a newborn can differentiate a recording of his mother's prenatal womb sounds from a recording of another mother (Righetti, 1996).

External sounds are also audible to the fetus. Much of our understanding of the intrauterine auditory experience comes from studies placing a recording device in the ear of a fetal ewe. As it turns out, sounds below 500 Hz (lower ranges of the human voice, violas, cellos, etc.) make it through the tissue with a small degree of *attenuation* (decrease in intensity), allowing the fetus to perceive, for instance, the father's voice, whereas sounds above 500 Hz that are comfortably loud for the mother are unlikely to be detected by the fetus (Gerhardt & Abrams, 1996).

The fetus also receives chemical sensory information in the womb. Flavors of food from the mother's diet are transmitted to the amniotic fluid and then swallowed by the fetus. This gives the fetus a chance to practice with flavors, helping to develop the systems of taste and smell. There is even evidence that these prenatal flavor experiences help drive post-natal flavor preferences. Babies whose mothers drank carrot juice during the third trimester of pregnancy showed more enjoyment upon first experience with carrot-flavored cereal than babies whose mothers drank water (Menella, Jagnow & Beauchamps, 2000).

Post-natal Development of the Nervous System: Infancy and Childhood

BRAIN DEVELOPMENT: SYNAPTIC DEVELOPMENT

A number of amazing patterns of development occur to the brain over the first year of post-natal life. In the first few months there is a rapid increase in the number of synapses. This comes as no surprise: perceiving and learning about the world necessitates the development of neural connections. Indeed, this increase in synaptic density continues throughout much of the first year of life. Around 1 year of age, though, the number of synapses in the brain begin to decrease, and continues to decrease until about 10 years of age, in a process known as **synaptic pruning** (e.g., Huttenlocher, 1994). But why would the brain want fewer synapses? It is suggested that this is an adaptive process: the brain defaults to produce an overabundance of synapses, and then prunes away the unnecessary or incorrect ones, thereby ensuring that the strongest and most useful survive. This can be likened to how a sculptor creates a statue with a block of stone and chisels away the unnecessary parts, rather than gluing pieces of sand together. The "chisel" in the brain could be many different things, such as various experiences or genetic signals.

There is much speculation about the experiential consequences of having extra synapses. How do extra synaptic connections affect the sensory experience of the infant? It does seem that at least some of the extra connections are functional. For example, in response to spoken language, the newborn's brain responses indicate activity in the auditory cortex, as well as just as much activity over the visual cortex, a pattern of activity that does not disappear until age 3 (Neville, 1995). Thus the infant may experience sensory information in an undifferentiated manner (reviewed in Spector & Maurer, 2009).

BRAIN DEVELOPMENT: ROLE OF EXPERIENCE

The rapid increase and decrease in synapses during early development is thought to be a method of sensory stimulation, necessary for the species typical development of the sensory systems. If one sense does not receive stimulation, often the extra connections are left open, so that the deprived sense can be supplemented by connections to other intact senses. That way, if an individual is born without one sense, for example, vision, then the brain can adapt by maintaining the "extra" connections between the visual and tactile areas that otherwise might have been pruned. This would allow the individual more neural processing surface area and a finer detailed representation of the world through the sense of touch so that the individual could almost "see with her hands". In fact, in individuals blind from an early age, the visual cortex is active when reading Braille and performing other tactile tasks (for reviews, see Amedi, Merabet, Bermpohl & Pascual-Leone, 2005; Maurer, Lewis, & Mondloch, 2005). Thus it seems possible that in the absence of visual input, the connections between the somatosensory and visual areas remain intact, so that the visual cortex is recruited for maximal tactile perception.

Further evidence for the role of experience in shaping neural development comes from studying the dendrites of animals raised in impoverished versus enriched environments. Such research began with the finding that rats raised in a more enriched environment, an environment with more sensory stimulation, are better at problem solving tasks such as maze learning (Hebb, 1949). This has a number of implications for children's development...but why does this happen? As it turns out, animals that are given enriched environments such as the opportunity to explore, or having their toys changed weekly, have increasingly complex neurons with more dendritic space than rats raised in barren environments (Diamond, Krech & Rosenzweig, 1964). Presumably, the increased complexity of the neurons comes from increased sensory processing in a complex and stimulating environment. This does not mean that individuals raised in poverty are not engaged in a stimulating environment; an *impoverished environment* refers to a lack of sensory stimulation, not socioeconomic status. If a developing child is given room to actively explore and is exposed to a lot of people, things, and new experiences, then it does not matter if he has a mansion or one bedroom apartment, whether he is playing with a ball of foil or a toy that lights up

Experience-Expectant / Experience-Dependent

The role of experience goes beyond the creation of neuronal connections, involving the general organization of the brain. For example, the visual cortex is organized into **ocular dominance columns** that synapse with neurons carrying information from each eye. In a typically-sighted individual, the area of dominance columns for both eyes is the same. Thus, receiving input from both eyes is **experience-expectant**, the brain expects there to be the same strength of input from each eye. If an animal has atypical visual development, and one eye sends more input than the other, then visual connections to each eye will be imbalanced. Thus, whether or not visual system connections and structures develop typically is **experience-dependent**, they will only develop typically if the animal receives the appropriate input. Nobel Prize winners David Hubel and Torsten Weisel found this when they deprived newborn kitten of vision to one eye for 2 months (Weisel & Hubel, 1963). The ocular dominance columns that synapsed with neurons from the open eye were much larger than the columns dedicated to the deprived eye. This is a laboratory analogue for what happens when a child is born with a cataract in one eye. When the cataract is removed, and the eye receives typical patterned visual input, the child's vision is still disrupted, presumably because of the lack of processing power in the ocular dominance columns receiving input from that eye due to previous deprivation If the individual is not treated for this disruption, then they will forever have a loss of visual acuity in the otherwise healthy eye, a condition known as **amblyopia**, sometime referred to as "lazy eye". Interestingly enough, the crucial treatment to avoid long-term visual problems once the cataract is removed is to cover the stronger eye (deprive it of visual input) for a period of time, known as "patching". Patching works because the eyes are competing with each other for cortical space. So even after regaining input to the deprived eye by removing the cataract, the stronger eye sends a stronger signal and the formerly deprived eye sends a weaker signal, thereby insuring the maintenance of current cortical status quo (uneven cortical processing space between the eyes). By removing input to the strong eye, a strong competitor for cortical space is removed, allowing the formerly deprived eye to strengthen its connections to the visual cortex. This allows the formerly weaker eye to develop its ocular dominance columns to the same level as the formerly stronger eye, and reduce the likelihood of there being a difference in acuity between the two eyes later in life (amblyopia) (reviewed in Maurer & Lewis, 2001a; also see Maurer & Mondloch, 2004)

BRAIN DEVELOPMENT: IMPLICATIONS FOR SENSORY DEVELOPMENT

Vision

At birth, infants have some crude visual abilities that, as discussed above, do not depend on visual experience. The visual acuity of a newborn is 40 times worse than that of a typical adult, mostly due to immaturity of the retina (Maurer & Lewis, 2001). By 1 month of age, an infant's visual acuity has increased to between 20/400 and 20/600, that is, they can see an object at 20 feet with the same amount of clarity that a typical adult can see at 400-600 feet. However, there are substantial and rapid postnatal improvements. Between birth and 6 months of age, there is a five-fold increase in acuity to just below adult levels of 20/20, followed by slow improvement to adult levels by 6 years of age (Maurer & Lewis, 2001). Retinal immaturity does not just affect visual acuity. Since the infant's structures responsible for perceiving colour are immature, a newborn has no color perception, and can only see in black, white, and shades of grey. Retinal immaturity does not just effect visual acuity though. At birth, since the infant's cones are immature, a newborn has no color perception, and can only see in black, white and grey. By 2 months their long wavelength cones have developed enough for them to see red, and by 3 months their medium and long wavelength cones have developed, and thus the ability to distinguish green and blue (Hamer & Varner, 1985).

Audition

In order to study infants' auditory capabilities, we must establish the intensity threshold at which they hear sounds of different frequencies. Audiologists do this by playing a tone of a certain frequency: they start with a low intensity tone and gradually increase the volume until the infant indicates that they can hear it. The lowest intensity level that an infant can hear becomes the threshold for that frequency. By repeating this procedure with all frequency ranges and a variety of babies, researchers have developed what is known as an **audibility curve** for infants.

At birth newborns have already had a substantial amount of experience with lower frequency ranges, and are much more sensitive to hearing lower frequencies. However, over the first 3 months of life, they show little improvement on lower frequencies, and rapid improvement on higher frequencies. By 3 months of age, sensitivity to higher frequencies has caught up and surpassed that of lower frequencies. In fact, there is no improvement on threshold for lower frequencies

(250 Hz) between 3-12 months, despite rapid improvement on higher frequencies. By 6 months, infants' thresholds approach adult thresholds on higher frequencies, though lower frequencies do not reach adult levels until school age or later (Oshlo, 1988). Thus the auditory system makes up for its lack of prenatal exposure to high frequencies by improving rapidly upon post-natal experience.

In addition to experience with lower frequencies, the infant is born with exposure to his or her mother's voice. As such, within 24 hours of birth, a baby will suck a pacifier to hear her mother's voice over another women's voice (DeCasper & Fifer, 1980). Newborns also seem to remember other auditory information heard in the womb as they tend to suck a pacifier to hear their native language by 2 days old (Moon, Cooper & Fifer, 1993) and to hear a story they heard in the womb (DeCasper & Spence, 1986).

Olfaction

Within hours of birth, babies show expected facial expressions in response to different odors; pleasant expressions for pleasant odors such as banana and vanilla, and unpleasant or disgusted expressions for unpleasant odors such as rotten eggs (Picture J.E Steiner, The Hebrew University, Jerusalem). This suggests that our olfactory system has certain innate sensitivities and preferences. However, newborns also show learned preferences for olfactory stimuli. 1-week old infants will turn towards nursing pads with their mother's milk on it significantly more than a nursing pad with another lactating woman's milk (MacFarlane, 1975). Presumably, breast milk has some of the same chemical makeup as amniotic fluid (Porter & Winberg, 1999), ingested by babies in the womb. Support for this idea comes from a study in which bottle-fed babies showed preference for the scent of their mother's amniotic fluid over the formula they have been given (Marlier, Schaal & Soussignan, 1998). Suggesting…

BRAIN DEVELOPMENT: SENSITIVE PERIODS

Several decades ago, evidence emerged in favor of the idea of critical periods during development. A critical period is a timeframe within which an organism must have certain input in order to develop optimally. For example, depriving an animal of visual input early in life results in long-term damage to the visual system and visual acuity and this damage persists even if input is restored (Hubel & Wiesel, 1970). Comparable disruptions later in life have no long-term effect. Based on these findings, a variety of scientists inferred that the nervous system loses plasticity after infancy, and if an organism is not raised in a species-typical environment, it will never have the opportunity to recover.

Some things definitely are better learned early in life. For example, recall from the chapter on language that the earlier an individual learns a language, the better the long-term fluency is. Consider that for individuals with visual deprivation due to cataracts, the earlier they establish input to the deprived eye, the better the long-term outcomes for visual acuity (Maurer & Lewis, 2005). But is it possible to learn a language later in life? Most definitely! Can people deprived of early visual input improve their vision later in life? They absolutely can. While early life does seem to be a time of greater sensitivity to change, the period of sensitivity does not abruptly end, but tails off gradually. As such, critical periods are now referred to as **sensitive periods**.

DEVELOPMENT OF THE NERVOUS SYSTEM: ADOLESCENCE

Adolescence marks a time of major change in the brain. Similar to the overproduction of synapses in the first year of life, there is another wave of synapse production in early adolescence and subsequent pruning (Giedd, Blumenthal & Jeffries, 1999). The greatest changes occur in the frontal lobes, which are responsible for self-control, judgment, emotions, and organization. The late development of this part of the brain may help to explain certain teenage behavior that adults can find aggravating, such as poor decision-making, recklessness, and emotional outbursts. Even more interesting is how the adolescent can have an effect on their own brain development, by using this time of rapid synapse development to "train" their brains for things like abstract thought, complex problem solving, physical activity, musical ability…or anything other than sitting on the couch and watching TV.

DEVELOPMENT OF THE NERVOUS SYSTEM: ADULTHOOD

For generations of brain research, scholars were taught that childhood was the only time in a person's life where new neurons could be created through a process known as **neurogenesis**. According to this dogma, if you did not maximize your brain development in childhood, you were out of luck. We now know that this is far from the truth. While neurogenesis certainly does not happen as globally or rapidly as it does in early childhood, adults can experience the growth of new neurons. Neurogenesis occurs continuously in discrete regions of the adult brain, particularly in areas of the hippocampus and the olfactory bulbs suggesting neurogenesis may play a role in learning and memory bulbs (Ming & Song, 2005). In response to injury and pathology such as strokes, traumatic brain injury, and neurodegenerative diseases, neurogenesis occurs in brain areas that are typically non-neurogenic (Ming and Song, 2005).

Experience-dependent plasticity also occurs in the adult brain. Some of the best evidence for this comes from studies of adults with **amblyopia**. Amblyopia is a condition resulting in poor vision in a seemingly healthy eye. This poor vision is due to unequal or abnormal visual input while the brain is developing in infancy and childhood. If the brain was not plastic in adulthood, then it is likely adults with amblyopia would have progressively worse vision with age. We now know that adults with amblyopia can improve their visual acuity via extensive practice on a challenging visual task (Levi, 2005). Further evidence for experience-dependent plasticity comes from studies of the visual cortex of typical sighted adults after a period of visual deprivation (blindfolding) (Pascual-Leone & Hamilton, 2001). Over the course of 5 days of blindfolding, sighted individuals were taught to discriminate tactile patterns. From day 2 onward, the visual cortex was increasingly active and the somatosensory cortex was decreasingly active during these tactile tasks (Pascual-Leone & Hamilton, 2001).

Such studies suggest that plasticity in the adult brain can help the brain adapt to change, such as injury or a decline in sensory functioning. Also important is the role of experience in plasticity. A common theme in brain development is the "use it or lose it" principle. You must give your brain things to do in order to drive plasticity. For example, physical exercise has been shown to stimulate brain cell development and connections (Kempermann et al., 1998) and reduce neural tissue loss (Colcombe et al., 2002). Aerobic exercise programs can improve the memory and sharpen the judgment of typically sedentary older adults (Colcombe and Kramer, 2003; Colcombe et al., 2004; Weuve at al., 2004).

Cognitive Development

Cognitive Development: Infancy and Childhood

Much of our modern understanding of cognitive development comes from the huge influence of a developmental psychologist by the name of Jean Piaget. Prior to Piaget's work, most individuals believed that children were different because they *knew* less than adults. Piaget systematically indicated that children's thinking is profoundly different than adults', and that development involved major age related changes in intellectual capabilities. Piaget proposed a trajectory of cognitive growth in four main stages, with children grasping more and more mature concepts at each stage. While many of Piaget's claims have been disputed, no lesson on cognitive development is complete without a discussion of Piaget – he laid the groundwork for everything we know about cognitive development including, importantly, how to ask the questions we are interested in.

Beyond Piaget: Modern perspective on Cognitive Development

Piaget's influence is undeniable; the order that he proposed human cognitive capabilities unfold has been found to be universal (Segall et al., 1990). What we have learned since Piaget is that development is a more continuous process than he suggested. Rather than skills appearing all of a sudden, they develop gradually, with primitive precursors to cognitive capabilities showing up perhaps even years earlier than Piaget would predict.

One thing we have learned is that Piaget underestimated infants' cognitive abilities. In fact, there is some evidence that babies are actually capable of some basic logic. Piaget's under-estimation of infants' abilities is exemplified by a particular series of experiments on the cognition of young infants. In one such experiment, infants were habituated to a rod moving back and forth behind a solid block (Figure #.12). Then the solid block disappeared and infants saw one of two test displays: a. an unbroken rod moving back and forth, or b. two aligned rod pieces move back and forth in unison. If the infants had perceived the original stimulus (rod moving behind solid block) as an unbroken rod, then test display a. would be nothing new to them, and test display b. would be a novel stimulus, one that should attract and hold their attention. Four month-olds spent more time looking at the broken rod than the unbroken rod, suggesting that they had perceived the parts of the rod in the original stimulus to be connected just as adults would (Kellman & Spelke, 1983; Kellman, Spelke & Short, 1986). Further evidence of infants' understanding of the physical properties of objects comes from studies showing that infants are surprised when seeing a car pass through a solid object, a ball stopping in midair and objects magically disappearing (Baillergeon, 1995; 1998; 2004; Wellman & Gelman, 1992).

In addition to understanding the physical properties of objects, infants seem to have a rudimentary understanding of numbers. For example, in one study 6 month olds were shown a series of slides that displayed different sets of 3 objects. The specific items on each slide changed (e.g., slide 1: comb, teddy bear, key; slide 2: pot, shoe, spoon), as did the spatial arrangement of the items, though every slide had 3 items. Infants were presented with these slides until they grew bored (habituated) of the slides of three (no small feat when you consider how many factors varied across slides). Once habituated to the slides of 3, infants were presented with a series of new slides, some of which contained two items and some of which contained three. Infants looked longer at the slides that contained 2 items over the slides that contained 3. Thus, infants are seemingly able to understand the one abstract concept that was constant across all slides i.e. the concept of 'threeness' (Starkey, Spelke & Gelman, 1983; 1990) indicating that infants are capable of a lot more than we often give them credit for.

Cognitive Development: Adolescence

Adolescence is a time of major physical and intellectual change. The beginning of adolescence is marked by an increase in the power of reason, giving young teenagers the capability to think about thinking, about what others are thinking, and thinking about what others are thinking about them.

During the early teen years, reasoning is often self-focused. Far from losing the egocentrism of childhood, many a teenager utters some variant on how parents could not possibly understand what it is like to be a teenager, despite parents having been teens in the not too distant past. Gradually, teenagers learn to focus their reasoning on the world, and thus learn the ability to reason about highly abstract concepts, such as good and evil, human nature, and justice. Adolescents' newfound ability to reason hypothetically allows them to develop abilities such as finding fault in others' reasoning and detecting hypocrisy, often leading to many a lively debate around the dinner table (Peterson et al., 1986).

Cognitive Development: Adulthood

INTELLECTUAL ABILITIES:

It is no secret that certain cognitive abilities decline with age. The speed and efficiency of intellectual processing, known as **fluid intelligence,** begins to slow down between thirty thirties. However, **crystallized intelligence**, an individual's accumulated knowledge, remains relatively stable over time, and may even increase with age as the individual gains more experience. What is more, even the documented decline in fluid intelligence is subject to broad individual variability, with some individuals maintaining their cognitive capabilities well into their seventies (Craik & Salthouse, 2000; Salthouse, 2000, Schaie, 1996; Verhagen & Salthouse, 1997).

What accounts for the large degree of individual difference in maintaining cognitive capability into older adulthood? Some theorists propose biological differences in cerebral blood flow, or death of neurons. Others suggest differences in education or the degree of neural stimulation in one's life. It is also possible that a decline in intellectual abilities could be related to a decline in working memory capacity, subject to individual difference, leading to a lesser ability to pay attention. Like any other aspect of development, individual differences in cognitive decline (or lack thereof) are no doubt subject to a dynamic interplay of genetic and environmental factors.

Leading thought used to claim that general cognitive decline is a natural part of aging, thus policies such as mandatory retirement age were developed. However, longitudinal studies of intelligence testing over time revealed that older adults' intelligence remained stable across the lifespan (Schaie & Geiwitz, 1982), and even increased on some tests. After all, let us not forget that some of our most important cultural contributors have been older adults. Grandma Moses did not start painting until she was 78, and Frank Lloyd Wright designed New York City's Guggenheim Museum at the young age of 89.

It is also important to remember that intelligence is not a single trait, but a number of distinct skills and abilities interacting. So how can we measure the decline of such a broad, complex concept such as intelligence? As we age, what we are losing in memory and processing speed, we are gaining in knowledge and verbal ability (Park et al., 2002). While it might take older adults longer to recall a word, they have a broader breadth of words from which to choose. Thus when we want a person who can process information quickly, perhaps we will call upon a younger adult, but if we want a person with deep knowledge of a subject, we will call upon an older adult.

AGING AND MEMORY

While the decline of memory is often considered a quintessential part of aging (ever heard your grandmother talk about having a "geriatric moment"), like intelligence, some aspects of memory remain intact throughout the lifespan. Younger adults surpass older adults on working and episodic memory (e.g., Crook & West, 1990; Earles, Connor, Smith & Park, 1998). However, implicit memory shows little or no decline with age. What older adults are asked to recall influences their likelihood of forgetting. If older adults are asked to recall a list of meaningless syllables or unimportant events, then they make more errors of recall than younger adults (Burke & Shafto, 2004). However, if the information is meaningful, then they have successful recall. As with intelligence, the variability in age-related memory decline is very broad, with some older adults as sharp as ever, and some displaying the memory deficits typically associated with old age.

Draft

Chapter 2

Evolutionary Psychology

Introduction

What *is* Evolutionary Psychology?

Evolutionary psychology is the pursuit of psychological science with explicit attention to contemporary knowledge and theory about the evolutionary process. In other words, evolutionary psychologists approach the study of mind and behaviour as a branch or subfield of evolutionary biology.

What justifies such an approach? Essentially, the answer is that **biology** is the science of life, encompassing everything that distinguishes living things from the inanimate world, and the theory of evolution is the unifying conceptual framework of biology. More specifically, there is no question that minds and brains, the objects of psychological science, have evolved according to the same principles that govern the evolution of anatomy and physiology, and just as evolutionary theories and knowledge provide useful guidance for researchers in these and other branches of biology, they can help direct research and discovery in psychology, too.

To illustrate what we mean, let's consider a particular evolutionary psychological study, conducted by Claus Wedekind and his collaborators, an experiment which may seem rather odd. In the first stage, male students at a Swiss university were recruited to be "odour donors". The men were given fragrance-free soap with which to shower, and plain, clean T-shirts, which they were instructed to wear on two consecutive nights. Each volunteer was told to sleep alone, and to refrain from eating garlic and spices. After two nights, he was to seal his T-shirt in a zip-lock bag and return it to the lab. A group of female students was also recruited, but their assignment was quite different: their job was to unzip the plastic baggies, sniff the contents, and rate the odours with respect to both their intensity and their pleasantness". In addition to these procedures, the researchers used molecular genetic techniques to determine the students' genotypes with respect to three particular genetic loci, namely members of the Human Leukocyte Antigen (HLA) group (also known as Major Histocompatibility Complex or MHC) genes. These particular genes play a role in immune function and were also known to affect body odours in mice and other mammals.

The shirts that the women were asked to rate had been worn by men who were either genetically similar to the rater in their MHC profiles or genetically dissimilar, and for purposes of analysis, the women were divided into two groups according to whether they were or were not taking oral hormonal contraceptives. The main results were as follows. Naturally cycling women (i.e. those not taking "the pill") rated the odours of men who were genetically dissimilar to themselves as significantly more pleasant than the odours of genetically similar men. However, women who were taking the pill showed precisely the opposite effect, rating the genetically similar men's odours as significantly more pleasant.

At this point, you're probably wondering what on earth this weird experiment was all about. Why would anyone even *think* of conducting it? Why did Wedekind suspect that a man's particular MHC genotype might affect how women would respond to his smell? And why did he think of assessing whether any such effects would then vary as a function of the woman's own genotype? Moreover, if the experimenters hadn't asked whether the women were taking oral contraceptives, the opposing effects that genetic similarity had on women's ratings as a function of whether they were "on the pill" would have washed each other out, making it appear that there were no effects at all. So what inspired the researchers to ask about contraceptive practices?

The answer to all these questions is that the hypotheses were derived from ideas about the evolved functions (or "purposes") of women's reactions to male odours. The first such idea is that a woman's choice of a mate can be influenced by her affective responses to male odours. The second is that there is a potential cost associated with being attracted to people whose MHC genes are similar to your own: couples who have similar MHC genotypes have an elevated likelihood of producing offspring with less versatile and therefore weaker immune systems (e.g. Penn *et al.* 2002), and natural selection should therefore have favoured preferences for partners who are dissimilar in this aspect of their genetic make-up. The third is that taking oral contraceptives puts women in an infertile psychophysiological state in which their affiliative preferences no longer reflect an evolved "strategy" for screening potential mates, but instead function in the realm of social support. Finally, you might wonder why the experiment was carried out with male odour donors and female raters rather than *vice versa*? The answer is that women, like most other female mammals, are typically more discriminating in mate choice than their male counterparts, apparently because bad choices are more costly to females, who must make a major investment in each successful offspring, than to males.

We have described this particular study here not so much because of the specifics of its rationale and its findings, but in order to illustrate two more general points. The first is that the things that Wedekind and his collaborators discovered are the same sorts of things that experimental psychologists without an evolutionary perspective are also trying to discover: previously unknown causal influences on psychological responses. In this case, these discoveries were, first, that self-similarity at certain genetic loci affects women's responses to male body odours, and, second, that the women's hormonal state exerts a modulating effect on these affective responses. The second point is that no psychologist operating without the heuristic benefit of evolutionary theories and knowledge could ever have discovered these facts. The hypotheses, which were supported by the data, were generated from an understanding of the adaptive functions that one would expect an evolved psychology of mate selection to be designed to accomplish.

Many further discoveries have followed from Wedekind's pioneering work, too many for us to summarize and discuss here. For a recent update, interested students can consult Havlicek & Roberts (2009).

TABLE #2.1	Understanding evolutionary psychology comes from an understanding of evolutionary theory in general; evolution provides a lens through which we can understand the human psyche;

Evolutionary Theory	Understanding & Predicting	The Influences of Evolutionary Psychology
• Our brains are a part of biology, and as a result, are as subject to the forces of evolution as all living things	• Through evolutionary psychology we can see how questions of adaptations and costs can affect our behaviour	• A number of questions in evolutionary psychology are questions that experimental psychologists in general ask, even if they are not informed or framed by evolutionary psychology
• Thus, our brains and our behaviour can be understood in light of evolution, as the result of factors and forces of natural selection	• Such questions lead to theories and predictions about the forces of natural and sexual selection in humans	• Being informed by evolutionary psychology, though, can help elucidate many problems and questions simply by understanding the brain and behaviour as subject to and the output of adaptive forces

Essential facts and ideas about evolution

The Concept of Evolution

Many lines of evidence indicate that populations of organisms change in various ways over generations. In other words, they **evolve**. One such line of evidence is provided by the fossil record of extinct plants and animals: in geological strata whose origins can be dated by a variety of methods, we see different life forms at different times in the past, and many of these extinct life forms can readily be arranged into series that appear to have been transformed over time. Another line of evidence is that both contemporary organisms and extinct ones can be readily and non-arbitrarily situated on a branching "tree", on the basis of structural similarity, a tree that is interpretable as a **phylogeny**: a pattern of divergence of distinct evolving lineages from common ancestors.

Phylogenetic trees can also be constructed on the basis of similarities in early development, such as the anatomical similarities of embryos of different species prior to birth, and they can also be constructed on the basis of similarities in DNA sequences, including sequences of non-transcribed "neutral" DNA. When independently constructed phylogenies of these various sorts are compared, they tend to be almost identical, which is exactly what we should expect if the magnitude of differences between two species is an indicator of the amount of time that has elapsed since they diverged from a common ancestor.

Evolution is often a slow process, such that it can take many thousands of years for significant change to become conspicuous. Even "rapid" evolution, such as the increase in cranial capacity and brain size in the genus *Homo* and its ancestors, occurred over the course of a couple of million years. It is therefore unsurprising that people often assert that the process of evolution is too slow to be observed directly, and can only be inferred. However, this is a misconception.

Although evolutionary change can indeed be glacially slow, it sometimes happens sufficiently speedily that it can be studied within the lifetime of an individual scientist. In rapidly reproducing micro-organisms, it can happen even faster: significant evolutionary changes can arise and sweep through populations in much less than a year, sometimes to our woe, as is the case when a disease organism rapidly evolves resistance to a previously effective antibiotic. But even among relatively large, complex organisms with generation times of more than a year, there are now dozens of well-documented examples of evolution in action. A particularly pleasing case is to be found in the results of longterm studies of the beak structure of a group of seed-eating birds known as Darwin's finches.

Darwin's finches comprise a closely related group of about eleven bird species belonging to a single genus. With one exception, they reside solely in the famous Galapagos Islands, about a thousand km off the west coast of South America in the Pacific Ocean. On a visit in 1835, Charles Darwin collected the first specimens of these birds known to science and shipped them back to London, where the ornithologist James Gould correctly inferred the several distinct species.

The Galapagos are volcanic islands that are less than ten million years old, and because of their remoteness, relatively few land animals have reached the archipelago and established themselves as breeding residents. One such species was the ancestor of Darwin's finches, and because few animals had preceded it there, it underwent an "adaptive radiation" into a variety of forms occupying ecological niches that would not ordinarily be available to a finch. One species, for example, became a hole-probing "Woodpecker finch", and another "Vampire finch" feeds on the blood of seals and other large animals! For the most part, however, Darwin's finches continued to do what finches typically do: forage for seeds on the ground. However, even the seed-eaters diversified to fill the subtly different niches occupied by co-residing finch species elsewhere, niches distinguished primarily by the size and hardness of the seeds they eat.

In 1973, Peter and Rosemary Grant began studies of Darwin's finches that continue to this day, paying particular attention to one species, the Medium Ground-Finch (Geospiza fortis) on one particular small island, Isla Daphne, and they soon documented a series of rapid evolutionary changes in the detailed beak morphology of this bird. In the mid-1970s, a severe drought on Isla Daphne greatly reduced seed production, causing finch populations to plummet. Not only were seeds scarcer, but the species composition of those remaining shifted: before the drought, the most abundant seeds were relatively small, soft Portulaca seeds, but by late 1977, most of what remained were large hard Tribulus seeds, and the only G. fortis that were capable of cracking them open were birds who happened to have unusually big beaks. The result was intense "natural selection": the birds that survived and bred were those with large beaks. Moreover, the Grants were able to demonstrate that beak size is "heritable", which means that offspring tend to resemble their parents in this trait. The result was that the whole distribution of beak sizes among Daphne's Medium Ground-Finches evolved to be noticeably larger within a generation.

Since their first exciting observations of rapid evolutionary change, the Grants and their students have documented other similar "micro-evolutionary" events, some of which were again due to weather-driven changes in the availability of particular foods, while others could instead be traced to changes in which particular competing finch species were also breeding on the island. It is gratifying that these particular birds, which played a role in inspiring Darwin's discovery of natural selection and its evolutionary effects, should have become a showcase of evolution in action.

The Theory of Evolution by Natural Selection

It is time to consider just what it was that Darwin discovered more than 150 years ago. The proposition that animal species evolve – that they undergo what Darwin called "descent with modification" over generations – was not a new idea. Many naturalists in Darwin's time were already contemplating this possibility, because it would provide a single, unifying explanation for the sequences of distinct fossils found in different geological strata, for the similar body plans and embryological stages of what were even then referred to as "related" species, and for the seemingly natural classification of animal species into "families" that could be organized into branching "trees". What was missing was a satisfactory theory of how and why evolutionary change and diversification might come about.

Darwin had the answer more or less worked out in the 1830's, but anticipating controversy and wishing to build an airtight case, he delayed making the theory public until 1858, when he was at last provoked to publish by the fact that another British naturalist, Alfred Russel Wallace, had arrived at essentially similar ideas. Darwin's and Wallace's great insight was that given certain uncontroversial premises, evolutionary change is an entirely predictable consequence of a blind, purposeless process that Darwin called "natural selection".

The first essential premise is that there is variation within natural populations: individuals of any given species differ, and some of the ways in which they differ may affect their survival and reproduction. The second essential premise is that offspring tend to resemble their parents in these variable attributes to some degree. They need not be (and of course are not) identical, but on average, parents and their offspring are more similar on pretty much any quantifiable trait than are two randomly selected members of the population. The third essential premise is that young are produced "in excess": in any species, more young are produced than will eventually become breeders in their turn or than would be necessary to maintain the population.

And that's all. From these three premises, each of which is demonstrably true, the process that Darwin called natural selection can be logically deduced, as can its potential to produce evolutionary change. If not all individuals reproduce (premise 3), *and* if those who do eventually reproduce are statistically more likely to have certain survival- and reproduction-promoting traits (premise 1), *and* if those traits tend to be transmitted to their young (premise 2), then useful traits are being "selected" by nature in a manner analogous to the selection for certain traits practiced by plant and animal breeders, and those useful traits will accumulate over generations and will tend towards optimal expression.

That is the gist of the idea of natural selection, and many writers since Darwin's time have suggested that it is more like a logical derivation than a falsifiable theory: natural selection *must* occur! That is true, but although it must occur, natural selection need not engender evolutionary change, and it often doesn't. If a population is well adapted to its ecological niche, then natural selection may be primarily *stabilizing*: a process that eliminates harmful departures from the optimal species-characteristic design, and thus *prevents* evolution. By this argument, the circumstance in which natural selection may be expected to produce evolutionary change is when ecological demands change. And that, of course, is precisely the circumstance under which the Grants documented rapid evolutionary change in the Medium Ground-Finches of Isla Daphne.

SECTION REVIEW: Essential Facts & Ideas about Evolution

TABLE #2.2	Evolution simply means changes that occur over generations of life forms; Darwin's theory of natural selection contributed to the understanding of how and why such changes occur

The Concept of Evolution	Evolution by Natural Selection
• **Phylogeny** is a method for understanding the history of evolution through the tracing of changes in species over time; it can be constructed on the basis of anatomical structures and/or DNA sequencing	• The first evidence for **natural selection** came from Darwin's observations of the differences and changes in the physical characteristics and behaviours of finches across the environments of the Galapagos islands
• Because major evolutionary changes occur over long periods of time, sometimes thousands of years, often it is assumed that the study of evolution is purely inferential and therefore direct empirical observation is inaccessible	• Darwin provided the how and why for the changes that occur through evolution
• Many evolutionary processes **can** be directly observed and used to support evolution since rapid changes also occur – sometimes over several generations, through a lifetime, or even over the course of a year	• **Variation** affects survival and reproduction through the **heritability** of traits; useful traits are selected and allow for reproduction and survival and through this propagate themselves into the future
• Additive microevolution = big evolutionary changes	• **Natural selection** is a stabilizing process – changes occur when necessary

Why Evolutionary Theory Matters to Psychological Design

Adaptations

Much as natural selection changes morphology over time, like the shape of bird beaks, it also alters behaviour. The waterflea, *Daphnia magna*, is a tiny crustacean that happens to be good food for some species of fish. To avoid predators, *Daphnia* engages in something known as "phototactic" behaviour: when the sun is visible in the sky, *Daphnia* sinks lower in the water to avoid being visually detected by fish predators; and when the sun has set, it floats closer to the water's surface to feed. Importantly, they are more likely to behave phototactically when the water contains chemicals excreted by fish predators (De Meester, 1993). That is, if there is no threat of predation (i.e. no chemical cues of predators nearby), *Daphnia* are likely to stay closer to the water's surface even where there is light out.

An interesting study of *Daphnia* eggs hatched from a pond that was stocked with fish during some years and not stocked with them during other years reveals that this flexible phototactic behaviour itself evolves as a function of the risk of predation (Cousyn, De Meester, Colbourne, Brendonck, Verschuren, & Volckaert, 2001). Offspring hatched from eggs that were laid by *Daphnia* when there were no fish in the pond responded less to light (i.e. they stayed closer to the surface) in the presence of fish chemical cues than did offspring hatched from eggs that were laid by *Daphnia* when there were fish in the pond. This means that *Daphnia* with genes that caused them to behave phototactically in the presence of fish predators were more likely to survive to lay eggs than *Daphnia* with genes that did not cause such phototactic behaviour. Conversely, when there was no threat of predation, *Daphnia* with genes that did not cause them to behave phototactically in the presence of fish predators were more likely to survive to lay eggs than *Daphnia* with genes that did cause such phototaxis.

Evolutionary psychologists, like many students of the behaviour of other species, sometimes call themselves "adaptationists". This label refers to the notion of **adaptation**: that many traits of organisms, both physiological and psychological, serve specific functions that benefited their bearers over generations by increasing their reproductive success, or **fitness**. Adaptationism is an approach to the investigation of organismal design in light of the notion that many aspects of an organism's **phenotype**—its appearance and behaviour—are the direct and indirect products of adaptations.

Functionality

In practice, what does a psychological adaptation look like? Much like a physiological adaptation (such as the eye or the heart), the psychological trait in

---

question should serve its purpose in an economical, efficient way, and its purpose should have led to an increase in fitness in ancestral environments. Unlike physiological adaptations, however, psychological adaptations may be more difficult to identify. One cannot, for instance, "see" mental mechanisms in the same way that one can "see" the mechanisms of blood vasculature—the heart, blood vessels, etc.—that allow for the distribution of molecules such as oxygen and nutrients to the body's tissues and organs. Instead, psychologists must infer the design of the putative adaptation from its outputs; that is, how it operates under specific conditions. Thus, hypotheses about psychological adaptations can be generated and empirically tested.

For example, consider the consequences of falling from a significant height for our human ancestors. Falling is painful and can cause physical damage, especially as the size of the fall increases with the distance between where one started and where one landed. One might hypothesize, then, that in addition to building a body that can better handle the shock of a fall, natural selection might also favour psychological mechanisms that led our ancestors to avoid falling large distances in the first place.

Russell Jackson and Lawrence Cormack (2008) hypothesized just this: that humans possess psychological adaptations whose function is to protect them from falling from great heights. Specifically, they hypothesized that people should perceive the distance between two locations in vertical space to be greater than it actually is, and that this misperception should increase as the viewer's perspective moves from a low position to a higher one. Jackson and Cormack found that observers perceived the distance between two vertical points to be larger when they made their estimates from a high vantage point than when they made estimates from lower vantage points, but they did not overestimate the distance between two points when made in horizontal space, irrespective of the height of the observer's vantage point. This novel illusion might help protect people from falls by inducing them to behave more carefully when moving around in high places.

Of course, psychologists already knew that there is functional design to the human psyche. Visual perception researchers make reference to "edge detectors" and "brightness compensation," and cognitive psychologists speak of memory "encoding" and "retrieval," "selective attention," and mental "processing." Even social psychologists have an implicit belief in functional design, replete with notions of "hedonic balance" and "cognitive dissonance reduction." But what's missing from the adaptationism of non-evolutionary psychologists is *selectionism*. Psychological adaptations, like physiological ones, don't serve simply to increase self-esteem, happiness, or some other aspect of overall well-being. Rather, they serve to increase fitness: the relative reproduction of an individual's genotype as a consequence of its traits.

It's important to be clear about what we mean when we say that psychological adaptations serve fitness interests. It simply means that organisms have mental traits, features, or attributes—they have sensations, perceive information, feel emotions, and make decisions—because their ancestors who had the same traits reproduced more successfully than other individuals in the population with different traits. It does not mean, however, that individuals know (consciously or unconsciously) that their psychological adaptations served this essential purpose in the past. Moreover, it does not mean that these adaptations continue to be reproductively advantageous in contemporary environments; the world has changed in many important ways over the last few thousand years, and our adaptations will in many cases lag behind. Finally, it does not mean that a psychological adaptation is perfect—just that it performed better (more efficiently, for instance) than other psychological traits for the same task.

Evolution-minded investigations of human psychology have led to a number of fruitful areas of research and important discoveries therein. Below, we catalogue a few of the better known discoveries made by considering the ways in which evolutionary theory can shed light on human psychology.

SECTION REVIEW: Why Evolutionary Theory Matters to Psychological Design

TABLE #2.3	Natural selection has a role in changing and affecting behaviour; the functional design of the human psyche exists as part of a greater system of fitness	
	Adaptations	**Functionality**
	• Natural selection has a role in changing and affecting behaviour	• Adaptations are economic and efficient, but their purposes, especially when it comes to psychology, are much harder to identify
	• Adaptations represent the role of traits in contributing to fitness through reproductive success	• The functions of adaptations are often inferred from their operations and corresponding hypotheses that have been empirically tested
		• The functional design of the human psyche is part of a greater system of fitness
	• Phenotypes, - appearances and behaviours- are useful for exploration as they are the direct outcomes of adaptations	• Our current traits exist because they have been inherited from ancestors with better reproductive success (better genes lead to greater chances of survival and reproduction)
		• Adaptations, however, are not continuously advantageous as the environment changes; they are not perfect just optimal for the environment in which they developed

Mate Choice and Sexual Jealousy

Sexual Selection

Evolutionary change is the consequence of differential reproduction, and so reproductive decisions are a core area of research for evolution-minded psychologists. Indeed, Darwin himself developed a theory designed specifically to address the apparent peculiarities of reproductive behaviour, which he dubbed **sexual selection**. Although Darwin originally conceived of sexual selection as a mechanism separate from natural selection, we now understand that it is really just a special form of natural selection, namely natural selection within the mating domain. This selection is a result of competition among individuals of one sex over access to the other sex ("intrasexual" selection) and competition to capture the interests of the other sex ("intersexual" selection).

With regard to intersexual selection, a particularly fruitful domain of research concerns **mate choice**: the psychology underlying whom to mate with. Those individuals who would be chosen most often by others as mates are those we might dub "attractive," but this raises an important question: what makes someone attractive?

Thinking in terms of evolved function helps to generate a number of hypotheses about attractiveness and mate choice. For example, what might an individual look for in mate? In part, the answer to this question depends on one's sex. To understand why, we will need to consider a fundamental reproductive difference between males and females. Sexual reproduction requires at least two sets of genes—one from each parent. These genes meet when the respective cells that they live in, called *gametes*, fuse together. Often, the gametes of the two parents are of different sizes: by definition, females produce the larger gametes, termed the ova (or eggs), and males produce the smaller gametes, termed the sperm.

Typically, females invest more in their offspring's development than do males. This begins with a larger investment in the ova, which, again, is larger than the sperm. But females will typically also gestate, feed, and nurture the offspring, often without any help from the males whatsoever. These differences in investment in offspring (and related differences between the sexes) lead to a profound difference between the optimal behaviour of the sexes: males benefit from attempting to reproduce more often than females, because males can re-enter the mating "pool" more often than can females (Clutton-Brock & Parker, 1992; Trivers, 1972). That is, because males invest less in offspring, a recently mated male can attempt to find a new mate and reproduce with her sooner than can a recently mated female.

This difference in the rate at which either sex can potentially reproduce has implications for the evolved design of human male and female sexual psychology. On average, men should be attracted to women who are likely to be able to reproduce soon and more often than other females, and men should tend to desire a greater number of mates (because they can benefit reproductively from having a greater number of sexual partners than can women). Conversely, women should on average be attracted to men who are likely to be able to invest in their offspring, and should desire fewer mates. Large-scale, cross-cultural research shows that this indeed is the case: men tend to prefer younger women (who are of reproductive age) and women tend to prefer wealthier, slightly older men (Buss, 1989). Moreover, men desire greater numbers of sexual partners and are more willing to engage in casual sex than women (Buss & Schmidt, 1993; Clark & Hatfield, 1989).

Evolutionary theory also generates hypotheses about more subtle differences in mate preferences, as well. First, if one function of a mateship is to produce offspring, then we would hypothesize that individuals would look for mates that show cues of reproductive ability, or *fertility*. Among both sexes, then, we might predict that people should generally prefer others of reproductive age: others old enough to reproduce but not so old as to be far outside of their reproductive primes. And if a concomitant function of a mateship is to produce "high quality" offspring—individuals with the best chance to survive and reproduce, themselves—then we would also hypothesize that individuals should prefer mates that present cues of "quality" as well, assuming of course that the quality of a parent is transmissible in at least some ways to his or her offspring.

CUES

But this raises another question: why would quality be transmissible from parent to offspring? The answer to this is that some individuals bear genes that make them better adapted to the local environment than others, and so their offspring who inherit these genes will, on average, also tend to be better adapted to the local environment. Thus, individuals should look for cues that an individual bears such locally adapted genes.

Researchers have identified a number of cues to fertility and quality, ones that others would probably not have considered without an evolutionary perspective. One such cue is known as fluctuating asymmetry, which is a measure of bilateral (left vs. right) traits that are symmetrical over the population as a whole, but not necessarily symmetrical for any given individual. The optimal body will tend to be symmetrical; it's more efficient to walk, for example, when both legs are the same length than when they're not. Over the lifespan, however, individuals are likely to encounter hardships, such as physical injuries and diseases, that affect their development in such a way that they become less symmetrical over time. Simply put, it's harder to maintain symmetry than it is to become increasingly asymmetrical. Individuals better adapted to the environment, however, should be more robust to such perturbations and develop more symmetrically than individuals who are less well adapted.

Related to fluctuating asymmetry is health. As discussed above, individuals more likely to succumb to disease will also tend to be more asymmetrical, so fluctuating asymmetry can be seen as one of several cues of health (Jones, Little, Penton-Voak, Tiddeman, Burt, & Perrett, 2001). The healthier an individual is, the better a choice of mate they will be for at least two reasons. The first is, as above, healthier individuals might be able to pass along the genes that helped keep them healthy to their offspring. Moreover, healthier individuals might make better long-term mates, because they can stay around longer and in better condition to help rear and support offspring. Hence, cues of health in general might be desirable in a prospective mate.

A third dimension that might be a cue of fertility and quality is how feminine or masculine an individual appears. To a large degree, femininity and masculinity are the consequence of differences in hormones that women and men have been exposed to over development. Although things are more complicated than this, men tend to have a much larger dose of testosterone during development than women, and women a much larger dose of estrogen than men. These hormones can affect a number of qualities, such as fertility and physical strength, and they will also tend to affect physical appearance correlated with biological sex, such that individuals exposed to more testosterone will tend to look more masculine and individuals exposed to more estrogen will tend to look more feminine. For instance, the waist-to-hip ratio (the circumference of the waist divided by the circumference of the hips) is strongly sexually dimorphic—women tend to have much narrower waists, relative to their hips, than men do. Thus, a waist-to-hip ratio is indicative of masculine/feminine characteristics, and women with lower waist-to-hip ratios have more estrogen and are more fertile than women with higher waist-to-hip ratios (Jasienska, Ziomkiewicz, Ellison, Lipson, & Thune, 2004).

Many studies have found that the cues discussed above—fluctuating asymmetry, apparent health, and masculinity/femininity—predict attractiveness. For instance, people prefer more symmetrical faces of real individuals as well as face images that have been altered to appear more symmetrical (Little & Jones, 2003; Penton-Voak et al., 2001; Perrett et al., 1999; Scheib, Gangestad, & Thornhill, 1999). Moreover, symmetry is associated with self-reports of personal health, and people tend to find apparently healthier faces more attractive (Jones et al., 2001).

Interestingly, women's attractiveness preferences vary as a function of their stage of the menstrual cycle. This may seem strange, but there is sound adaptive logic underlying such menstrual cycle shifts. Humans, unlike many other primates, generally rear offspring in mated pairs, consisting of the offspring's genetic mother and (putative) father. However, women are faced with a tradeoff in their choice of a mate: some men may have "quality" genes that they can transmit to their offspring, but they are not necessarily valuable as long-term mates, because they are not as willing or as capable of investing in the offspring, or because they are already mated. If the ideal mate with both quality genes and the desire and means to invest in offspring is not available, a pragmatic alternative is available. A woman could mate with one man to produce her offspring and marry another man to help support them.

However, men are typically less interested rearing the offspring of their mate's paramours (Wilson & Daly, 1992; see also "Kinship and human affairs," below). Thus, a woman pursuing a strategy of cuckoldry—whereby her long-term mate (such as her husband) is led to believe that another man's children are his own—needs to have some method of gaining access to high quality genes while keeping a hold on her long-term mate. As it turns out, shifts in preferences for a mate over the menstrual cycle may be the solution.

Women are only fertile for a few days each month, during a phase of the cycle known as *ovulation*, so their decisions about with whom to mate might vary as a consequence of whether they run an increased chance of becoming pregnant. Thus, we might predict that women would be most concerned with certain qualities of physical attractiveness when they are ovulating, and be more concerned with other benefits (like the long-term investment potential of a mate) during other phases of the cycle (Gangestad & Thornhill, 2008).

This indeed seems to be the case. Ovulating women, relative to women who are not ovulating, tend to have stronger preferences for facial masculinity (Johnston, Hagel, Franklin, Fink, & Grammer, 2001; Penton-Voak et al., 1999). At ovulation, women's short-term preferences also shift towards being attracted to men who are more confident (Gangestad, Simpson, Cousins, Garver-Apgar, & Christensen, 2004) and talented (Haselton & Miller, 2006), but their long-term preferences were relatively unchanged by menstrual cycle phase. And, perhaps most amazingly of all, ovulating women even tend to prefer the *smell* of symmetrical men, though they were never exposed to anything other than a T-shirt that the men in the study wore (Thornhill & Gangestad, 1999).

INFIDELITY

Until very recently, with some sophisticated technological advances, any fetus that a woman carried was guaranteed to be her own genetic offspring. Thus, women could be completely certain of their maternity. Not so for men: because fertilization is internal in humans (unlike many fish species, for example, in which males fertilize a females eggs outside of her body), a woman may mate covertly with a man other than her long-term partner, so men could not have been certain of their paternity (again, until recent technological advances). There is even an old saying for this: "mama's baby, papa's maybe."

As it would have been in a man's fitness interests to invest in his own genetic offspring more so than the offspring of another man, male psychology should have evolved to avoid being the victim of cuckoldry. Thus, evolution-minded psychologists predict that male and female sexual psychology should again differ in an important way: how the two sexes respond to sexual infidelity.

Men risk losing fitness when their mates have sexual relations with other men. However, as discussed above, women risk losing fitness when their mates take resources out of the relationship and invest those resources into relationships with other women. By consequence, men should be more prone than women to *sexual jealousy*—feelings of anger and a desire to "guard" a mate or sexual prospect from engaging in sexual activity with potential rivals. Conversely, women should be more prone than men to *romantic jealousy*—feelings of anger and a desire to "guard" a mate or sexual prospect from leaving the relationship to form a new one with potential rivals.

Imagine the following two scenarios, as one study (Buss, Larsen, Westen, & Semmelroth, 1992) asked participants to do: (1) your long-term, romantic partner forming a deep emotional attachment to another person; or (2) your partner enjoying passionate sexual intercourse with that other person. It is likely that you would find both scenarios would distressing, but the question at hand is *which would distress you more?* When research participants are asked to choose between the two, men were significantly more likely than women to choose scenario (2), that their partner having sexual intercourse with someone else was more distressing than their partner finding deep affection elsewhere. Conversely, women were significantly more likely to choose scenario (1) as being more distressing than scenario (2).

The same pattern—men being more sexually jealous, on average, than women—has been replicated in several other cultures (Buunk, Angleitner, Oubaid, & Buss, 1996). But it has also been evaluated in "real-world" contexts. If sexual jealousy has been designed by natural selection to reduce a man's risk of cuckoldry, then men should respond to cues of such risks in "jealous" ways. Flinn (1988) showed exactly this when he recorded, at regular intervals, the behaviour of those he came across in a Carribean village: being mated to a "fertile" woman (i.e., a woman of reproductive age and who was not currently pregnant, and could thus become pregnant) leads to more conflict within the relationship—especially if the relationship was not sexually exclusive—and more conflict with sexual rivals.

This conflict over a man's sexual exclusivity over his mate can escalate quite dangerously, leading to domestic assault and homicide. Sexual jealousy is a common motive for domestic violence, and it is far more commonly the cause of male-perpetrated violence than female-perpetrated violence (Daly, Wilson, & Weghorst, 1982). Moreover, historical laws in a variety of different places consider adultery—a violation of sexual exclusivity—a crime against the husband or male partner in a relationship, but often do not accord women the same legal protection (Wilson & Daly, 1992). In fact, many legal systems once considered women to be the property of men—the property of their fathers before marriage and the property of their husbands once married. It is only as women have demanded and achieved a legal status equivalent to that of men that men have been obliged to acknowledge women's agency and right to autonomy.

SECTION REVIEW: Mate Choice and Sexual Jealousy

TABLE #2.4

Differences among the sexes influence parental investment as well as mate preferences, mate selection, and responses to mate behaviour

Sexual Selection	Cues	Infidelity
• **Sexual selection** and the resulting differential reproduction is a special form of natural selection based on competition to mate and reproduce	• Different sexes look for different cues of reproductive ability to find a mate of the best quality for gene transfer	• There exists increasing uncertainty from men about offspring as they have less reliable cues than females and face greater costs of investing in the offspring of other males
• The study of mate choice is essentially the study of the underlying psychological mechanisms that guide attraction and mating	• Cues of **fluctuating asymmetry** are indicative of health and robustness towards environmental hardship	• As a result of differential investment and paternal uncertainty, there exist differential responses to infidelity; men are more threatened by sex whereas women are more threatened by romance
• Attraction is a factor of the sex of individuals: their gamete sizes and differential parental investment	• This, in combination with cues of reproductive ability, such as levels of masculinity and femininity, contribute to attractiveness ratings	• Jealousy by men is often the reason for domestic assault and homicide by men
• Females typically provide greater investment, whereas males seek out multiple partners; this in turn affects the evolution of sexual psychology and differences in	• Cues of mate quality and preferences vary i.e. through the menstrual cycle	
	• Differential concerns exist at different points in the life cycle	

attraction		

Kinship and Human Affairs

Social Behaviour

In the 1960s, the study of biology was revolutionized once more by the work of theoreticians trying to understand the evolution of *social behaviour*—actions that affect not just the individuals performing them, but other individuals as well. Performing an action in one's own self-interest can easily be understood in Darwinian terms: if an individual performs a behaviour that improves its own fitness, then the genes promoting it would be selected for, and the behaviour would eventually become widespread. What is less obvious, however, is why organisms have apparently evolved to help *others* in at least some species and some contexts.

To understand the problem, imagine a gene that leads its bearers to give up some of its resources to any other individual it encounters. All individuals with this gene willingly decrease their own fitness by gifting their resources to others, whereas the recipients of these gifts gain in fitness for such generosity. As the "generous" gene is in competition with other, less generous genes in the population, it will inevitably disappear from the population as its bearers are at a selective disadvantage relative to the bearers of other genes. It is simply not obvious why selection would ever favour a gene that caused its bearers to help others, and yet we can see helping behaviours everywhere we look.

A striking example of helping behaviour is found among the eusocial insects, such as ants, termites, and some bee and wasp species. Though there are many differences among these species, what makes them all "eusocial" is that all have a radical reproductive division of labour: a minority of individuals reproduce, and the remainder are sterile. These sterile individuals are workers that, among other things, help to defend the colony and rear the young. It is difficult to imagine a more "generous" gene than one that causes chronic sterility in its bearers in order to promote the welfare of others; yet, such genes have not only thrived in certain corners of the natural world but have in fact arisen repeatedly and been replicated for eons. How is this possible?

The key to the evolution of social behaviour—whether helping or harming—comes from thinking about evolution not in terms of individuals or groups, but from the perspective of the genes themselves. To say that a gene has been selected for is to say that it becomes more numerous than its rivals (other genes) in the population over generations; that is, there are more copies of some genes than others over evolutionary time. One way in which a gene may proliferate is by ensuring that its bearers get more than their fair share of resources, increasing the probability that they will survive to reproduce more copies of the gene for future generations.

Alternatively, a gene can proliferate by helping copies of itself in other bodies. Consider a gene that that leads its bearers to give up some of its resources to other individuals *bearing copies of itself*. If the cost, in fitness terms, to the gene responsible for the helping behaviour is sufficiently small and the benefit to those gene copies receiving the help is sufficiently large, then there will be more copies of the gene in future generations. In other words, natural selection can favour helping behaviour after all.

We need to be more precise, of course, than "sufficiently small" and "sufficiently large." Just how small ought the cost to the individual performing the action (the *actor*) be? And how large the benefit to the recipient? Let us call the fitness cost to the actor c, and the benefit to the recipient b. Obviously, if selection is to favour helping behaviour, the cost to the actor (and the gene promoting the behaviour) must be less than the benefit to the recipient, so $c < b$; otherwise each time the actor helps the recipient, there will be increasingly fewer copies of the gene promoting the helping behaviour. This condition isn't quite enough, though, to lead to positive selection on a helping gene. Recall that an indiscriminately "generous" gene that leads its bearers to help any recipient in the population, willy nilly, would be selected against, but a gene that caused its bearers to help recipients bearing copies of itself could flourish. Thus, we need some measure of the probability that the recipient does in fact carry copies of the gene promoting the helping behaviour. This measure is known as **genetic relatedness**.

Genetic Relatedness

Genetic relatedness, r, refers to the likelihood that the recipient and actor carry identical copies of a gene involved in the behaviour of interest (i.e. helping or harming). Moreover, r is measured against *chance*: the average probability that an individual might carry copies of the gene. This is because a social behaviour will only be favoured by selection if it increases the relative frequency of the gene responsible for it. Think of it like this: the average, or mean, frequency of a gene over successive generations will not change if only the average number of copies of it are added to it, in the same way that the mean of 1, 3, 1, and 3 is the same as the mean of 2, 2, 2, and 2. When two individuals are more likely than chance to carry the same genes, they are said to be "positively related," because they are more related than we would expect by chance alone ($r > 0$). Conversely, when two individuals are less likely than chance to carry the same genes—in other words, they are more likely to carry *rival* genes—they are said to be "negatively related," because they are less related than we would expect by chance ($r < 0$).

Genetic relatedness can be thought of as an exchange rate that translates money from one currency into another (Frank, 1998). In the case of genes, r translates the value of the recipient's reproduction into the actor's reproduction. The greater the probability that the recipient shares copies of a gene responsible for an actor's behaviour, the more related the two individuals are, and the more valuable the recipient's reproduction is to the actor (because the recipient's reproduction leads to more copies of the gene being produced). Returning to the problem of when to help others, then, we can incorporate r into our scheme of costs and benefits. The benefit to the actor's *genes* of helping a recipient is a consequence of the recipient's relatedness to the actor; thus, we need to weight the benefit of a social action to that recipient by r. In other words, the cost to the actor must be less than the benefit to the recipient multiplied by the relatedness between the two, or $c < rb$.

This simple formula is known as Hamilton's rule. It is named after W. D. Hamilton, the theoretical biologist who identified the problems of sociality and developed **inclusive fitness theory** to explain it. Inclusive fitness theory is a way of accounting for the evolution of social behaviour by measuring the success of a hypothetical gene promoting the behaviour via its effects on its bearers (the actors) and on copies of itself in the bodies of others affected by the behaviour (the recipients). An actor's fitness is thus determined by the effect of its actions on its own reproduction (direct fitness) and on the reproduction of recipients (indirect fitness); the sum of these two components of fitness is the actor's "inclusive fitness." Following the logic shown above, direct fitness is represented by c and indirect fitness is represented by *rb*.

SECTION REVIEW: Kinship and Human Affairs

TABLE #2.5	Social behaviour can also be understood as a function of natural selection; incurring costs to ourselves for the benefit of others is a factor of inclusive fitness

Social Behaviour	Genetic Relatedness
• The evolution of **social behaviour** is also of high interest and can be understood through evolutionary theory	• We help the propagation of our own genes by helping those who share our genes – our genes will still be copied to a large degree
• One question that doesn't seem to make sense in light of natural selection is: Why do people help others?	• Such social behaviour is based on measures of **genetic relatedness** (the percentage of shared genes) as well as precise measures of the costs of helping others and the benefits
	• The costs must be less than the benefits (as a factor of genetic relatedness)
• In order to understand the answer we need to think of evolution at the level of the gene, not individuals or groups	• **Hamilton's Rule**: $C < RB$
	• Such information has lead to the development of the theory of **inclusive fitness** – overall fitness is determined by both direct and indirect fitness

Inclusive Fitness

Inclusive Fitness & Behaviour

Inclusive fitness theory revolutionized the way biologists and many social scientists think about sociality. It provides a conceptual framework to help us understand the evolution of behaviour and, with it, many otherwise puzzling behaviours could be explained by the simple idea that organisms evolved to pursue courses of action that were in the best interest of their genes. For instance, it explains the evolution of eusociality in insects, as mentioned above: eusociality has evolved only in species where reproductive individuals (e.g., queens) mated monogamously—that is, with only one male—which leads to high positive relatedness ($r > 0$) among the progeny (Hughes, Oldroyd, Beekman, & Ratnieks,

2008). Moreover, the benefits of helping are large relative to the costs, so $b > c$ (Queller & Strassman, 1998).

Inclusive fitness theory has also been of great help in understanding human psychology and behaviour. A case in point regards the study of lethal violence. A hypothesis one can generate from inclusive fitness theory is that organisms should have evolved to care more for genetic relatives than for other individuals: individuals should bestow more benefits to positive relatives, such as close kin, and protect them from harm. Thus, we might expect individuals to be discriminative with respect to the recipients of their affections.

Target Study: FAMILY HOMICIDE

Researchers: Martin Daly and Margo Wilson (McMaster University)

Source: Daly, M. & Wilson, M. (1988). Evolutionary social psychology and family homicide. *Science, 242,* 519 – 524.

Note: The material below is the author's summarized description of the original published article.

One particularly disturbing and puzzling aspect of human behaviour is the occurrence of family violence, homicide in particular. By applying the framework of evolutionary psychology, the researchers work to come to a better understanding of why such behaviour. Given what we know about the role and functioning of inclusive fitness, something like family violence seems contradictory though, or at least counterintuitive. However, more thorough analyses of the specific factors involved can shed light on why what occurs actually seems to make sense if evolutionary theory is given serious consideration.

Homicide is one of the most extreme forms of conflict, and the phenomenon of family violence has been fascinating to many, questioned throughout human history. Of all social groups, the greatest amount of violence is seen in families, and this prominence in and of itself is enough to warrant it worth studying. However, this prominence is also quite confusing. Aren't we nepotistic towards our family members? Isn't inclusive fitness, *not* family violence the result of selection pressures? Family violence does, however, begin to make sense once it is looked at in terms of the particular relationships involved and factors such as genetic relatedness of family members are considered. It is easy to forget that talk of family violence includes non-blood relatives. Genetic relatedness has been shown to be a predictor of both levels of co-operation and conflict - the greater the level of relatedness, the greater the likelihood that conflict will be mediated. Nonetheless conflict of interest still occurs amongst blood relatives and can contribute to family violence as well.

METHODS

The authors chose homicide as a representative of family violence with two main advantages in mind: the serious of its nature and the extent to which individuals therefore care about the phenomenon, as well as the fact that because of its degree of seriousness, the data available on homicide cases is a lot less biased than other forms of family violence. In order to operationalize 'family' for the purposes of the study, the researchers limited the family unit to co-residing relatives, both genetic and non-genetic. This definition limits the scope and generality of the research while still being inclusive of the reality that not only genetic relatives are considered part of a family. The approach taken in this research involves analyses of homicide rates in terms of two general contexts: genetic relatedness versus non-genetic relatedness in co-residency, and the role of conflict of interests in determining the likelihood of violence (homicide) in genetic relatives. In terms of comparisons between genetic and non-genetic relatives, the researchers analyzed general levels of homicide, step-relationships, and spousal conflicts. In terms of conflict amongst genetic relatives, the researchers explored different situations of parent-offspring conflict. Data collection involved observational analyses of homicide records - patterns of relationships amongst incidences of homicide and non-lethal violence were measured. The particular relationships involved and the levels of relatedness were critical factors used for providing thorough analysis of family violence. Factors such as socioeconomic status, individual health, and other demographic variables were also taken into consideration. Analyses were performed on homicide data from the early-to-mid 1970s to the early-to-mid 1980s on populations mainly in the United States and Canada, as well as British, Australian, and indigenous South American populations.

RESULTS AND DISCUSSION

Overall, the researchers found that even within co-residency, genetic relatedness is a strong predictor of homicide rates. Victims and killers co-residing are more likely to be non-genetic relatives than genetic relatives. On the other hand, homicides involving co-killers (co-operation) are significantly more likely to involve genetic relatives than non-genetic relatives. This indicates that co-residency in and of itself is not a confound that would bias towards an increase in homicide rates among family members simply because of increased access and opportunity; there are other fundamental factors at play that differentiate levels of violence even within homes.

Step-relatives

Children co-residing with stepparents are more likely to be neglected and abused than the genetic children of stepparents. Occurrences of homicide are rare, however when they do occur, violence is increasingly more likely to be directed at stepchildren. This I believed to occur because of stepchildren's decreased reproductive value for stepparents in comparison to their genetic offspring.

Spousal Conflicts

Spouses often develop relationships of mutual interest and benefit because of shared relatedness to common offspring. However, there are incidences where this relationship is threatened, and the benefits of co-operation are outweighed by certain costs. This includes the threat of infidelity, the possibility that one parent has been tricked into investing in non-genetic offspring. This also includes the investment of one spouse into children from previous mates, posing a cost rather than a benefit to the other spouse, paving the way for future possible conflict perhaps over the allocation of resources. Male jealousy is one of the most threatening and dangerous forms of family violence. The younger wives are, the more likely they are at risk because of their increased desirability (being more fertile than older women) and the lower likelihood that a deep bond has been fostered between the spouses, especially if there are no offspring.

Parent-offspring Conflict

Although rates of violence and homicide have been shown to be distinctly lower for genetic relatives, incidences still arise in particular contexts, and potential explanations exist to help understand why. Parent-Offspring conflict in general arises because of differential desires for the allocation of parental resources (best for parents to divide resources equally and best for each offspring to gain as much resources as possible). Infanticide, the killing of young offspring, often occurs when the condition of offspring demands a greater cost from parents than the benefits that they will receive. Major factors involved in infanticide include uncertainty of parenthood, poor quality of offspring, and extrinsic factors such as socioeconomic issues. Filicide, the killing of offspring by parents, tends to decrease with offspring age, likely because offspring are increasingly closer to sexual maturity and more likely to reproduce, thus benefitting the genes of the parents.

Patricide, the killing of parents by offspring, is often the result of extrinsic factors such as socioeconomic issues, or occurs as a response to violence from parents.

Limitations

Although the analyses performed in this study have been informed by evolutionary theory, they are still limited in terms of what they can conclude because they are observational in nature. The patterns of results appear to fall in line with the predictions of evolution, yet we must be wary of falling prey to the confirmation bias. Yes, the relationships that lead to increased occurrences of violence are clear, but **why** they occur in this way is not clear cut and absolute.

The samples used are cross-cultural, however, they are still limited in their scope as they are mainly Western centric. We must keep in mind the possibility that social factors might interact with inherent evolutionary factors in unexpected ways that are not revealed by this study.

As well, we must be cautionary about what the data is telling us. The researchers aren't taking a look at all families and their dynamics of conflict and co-operation; they are focusing in on cases of violence, mainly homicide, which itself is rare. Simply, it is important to be aware of this distinction, as it may alter perceptions of, for example, stepparent families that are actually comprised of co-operative and nepotistic relationships.

Comments

Despite the fact that it is difficult to conclusively infer from the results the reasons as to why patterns of family violence, particularly homicide, occur in the way that they do, evolutionary theory still provides a framework through which we may be able to predict, interpret and understanding this phenomenon. The role of self-interests seems to be critical; the outweighing of benefits by costs may be the most important motivating factor for acts of violence and helps to explain the different levels of violence between genetic and non-genetic relatives. It is worth noting though that behaviours that occur are not always adaptive, and this applies to homicide as well. Often violent behaviours have negative social repercussions, such as imprisonment, but thousands of years of selection have lead us to continue to exhibit tendencies and behaviours that may be maladaptive in present-day. Evolutionary psychology shows itself to be useful in understanding and predicting patterns of family violence, but it also highlights that research is far from complete, and the predictions suggested must be extended to other domains in order for the robustness and generality of the claims to be tested.

In summary, incidences of family homicide deal with situations of conflict of interest, and are affected by levels of genetic relatedness and the costs incurred by particular genetic relations. Genetic violence still occurs, it is just less likely because more often than not, relatives provide greater benefits than costs. According to evolutionary theory, one way of understanding family homicide is in terms of the costs and benefits involved in certain relationships, whether genetic or non-genetic relatives are involved.

Lethal violence can serve as a window on cooperative sentiments by studying where such sentiments fail. Although homicide is not common, it is drastic and frequent enough for it to shed light on human cooperation. Applying what we know about inclusive fitness theory to homicide, we might predict the following: the victims of violence should be less related to the perpetrators than other potential victims. That is, people should be more willing to harm nonrelatives than their kin. And indeed this is the case: people are far more likely to kill unrelated acquaintances and strangers than relatives. More to the point, not all "relatives" are equally likely to be the victims of homicide: individuals are far more likely to kill their spouses and step-children, who are not genetically related, over their genetic offspring or other genetic relatives in the household (Daly & Wilson, 1988). Interestingly, this logic extends to "collaborative" homicide, where two or more individuals help each other to kill another person. In such cases, collaborative killers tend to be more genetically related to each other than to their victims (Daly & Wilson, 1988).

Of course, violence is not the only window on the importance of biological kinship to human affairs. Inclusive fitness theory predicts that humans, among other organisms, should be generally nepotistic, in accordance with the rule $c < rb$. Thus, we expect that when individuals pay a cost, they should be more willing to do so to help genetic relatives than to help nonrelatives. And indeed this is the case. For instance, when told that four people are trapped in a burning building and that you can only save one, which person we choose to save will depend on their genetic relatedness to us: we are more likely to state that we will save a close relative, like a sibling or parent, than a more distantly related individual, like a cousin or an acquaintance (Burnstein, Crandal, & Kitayama, 1994). Moreover, the relationship between willingness to help and genetic relatedness is stronger when the consequences of the decision are more serious, as when the costs to the actor or benefits to the recipient increase (Burnstein et al., 1994; Stewart-Williams, 2007).

But perhaps people in these studies are simply claiming that they'd help their relatives without really knowing what they would actually do if they had to rush into a burning building and could only save one of several people trapped inside. Is there any evidence from the "real world" that people are helpful in nepotistic ways, as inclusive fitness theory would lead us to expect?

The answer again is "yes." Among the Ye'kwana of Venezuela, for example, individuals provide a substantial amount of effort to tend to their neighbours' gardens, a source of much of the food for each household. As expected, there is a positive correlation between the amount of help an individual provides to a neighbouring household and the average relatedness of that household to the helping individual (Hames, 1987). Similarly, South African migrant workers tend to send more money back home when to their families when them members of their households comprise more genetic relatives (Bowles & Posel, 2005).

Application Box:
The Naturalistic Fallacy

Science, including natural selection, only describes what **is**, not what **ought** no be. Natural selection makes a number of general claims about adaptive behaviours, but these behaviours arose out of responses to environmental changes, they are certainly not deterministic and they may prove to no longer be optimal in new environments. Despite this, a number of contentious issues have arisen due to misconceptions since Darwin's first publications on natural selection, and continue to exist today.

One issue associated with natural selection is the Social Darwinism movement (associated quite unfortunately with Darwin, although it is Herbert Spencer who is responsible). Social Darwinism arose out of beliefs that natural selection was about survival of the fittest. Individuals with good strong traits would and should survive, and those without should be weeded out. Such misconceived views have been used to justify practices such as colonialism, class division, and inbreeding, but the so-called justification is based on misguided perceptions about both the operation of natural selection as well as beliefs in genetic determinism. With a deeper understanding of the processes of heredity, its intricacy and complexity is immediately realized; traits are not based on single genes that must be preserved as once thought. Reproduction can result in such a wide variety of outcomes that it is nearly impossible to predict what any instance of fertilization will produce. Social Darwinism falls prey to the errors of the naturalistic fallacy by assuming that what is natural is good and ought to be preserved. The claims made in evolution about human behaviours are generalizations. We do not necessarily have the most optimal traits or behaviours for our current environment; a lot of things are remnants from our evolutionary past; not every trait or behavior is adaptive or works perfectly. Also, generalizations represent averages of traits or behaviours, and often we fail to consider the great amount of variability that exists. The 'ideal' is often more rare than the variability around it; strict dichotomies are exceptional in nature, but they aid in formulating general theories. Also, traits are not deterministic; even patterns that have evolved over thousands of years are in continuous interaction with the environment may become modified over a lifetime. What is natural is not what is good, what is natural is just what is; successful genes are successful because they have survived, perhaps they are not adaptive and perhaps one day they will cease to exist. Because natural selection itself does not follow any sort of moral code in the sense that we conceptualize morality, social Darwinism and the naturalistic fallacy are not legitimate in and of themselves or legitimate grounds for basing any sort of morality or moral codes.

Another important issue to consider in relation to the misconceptions of natural selection and their dangerous consequences is eugenics. Eugenics is a practice that promotes the selection of desired traits through constraints on reproduction, and even elimination of individuals with undesirable genes. Although more of a prominent issue in the earlier half of the 20th century, eugenics continues to be a threat especially with the development of technologies that allow for prenatal screening and genetic testing. Unlike social Darwinism, eugenics pushes the view that natural selection should be tampered with to enhance survival of the fittest. The results of eugenics, however, are only uninformed views about evolution and genetics as well as issues of racism and sexism.

Eugenics claims to promote the existence of desirable genes and traits while eliminating undesirable genes and traits in order to transform the human species into the best state possible. But given what we know about how natural selection actually operates, how could we ever truly define absolutely desirable traits? And even if some sort of widespread agreement was established on this, how could we implement eugenic practices without violating human rights laws? Eugenics just doesn't sit right, and for good reason.

Kin Recognition

Nepotistic discrimination raises some interesting questions for psychologists about **kin recognition**, the psychological mechanisms that organisms have to help determine how closely related they are to others. It might seem obvious to you that you've come to identify your relatives simply as those individuals whom you've been told are your kin—your parents, your siblings, aunts, uncles, grandparents, cousins, and so forth—but it seems that the ways in which we recognize kin are more complicated than this, as we'll see below.

So, how do we come to recognize our relatives? From an evolutionary perspective, we might expect organisms to use *cues* of kinship—aspects of themselves, their environment, or others that would have been reliably associated with actual relatedness—to identify kin. For instance, in our evolutionary past, a woman was the genetic mother of every baby she gave birth to; on this basis, we could predict that women will identify any individual they birthed as their offspring. Likewise, since women are the primary caregivers in every society on Earth, and the same is true of closest primate relatives, we could predict that babies will come to recognize their primary female caregiver as their mother.

And what about one's siblings? As children tend to live with their mothers, older siblings can learn to recognize younger siblings as those newborn offspring that their mother takes care of, a cue known as "maternal-perinatal association" (Lieberman, Tooby, & Cosmides, 2007). However, as older children are somewhat more independent of their mothers, younger children require some other cue to help identify their older siblings. Since siblings are typically reared together in the same household, co-residence duration may provide a useful kinship cue: the longer two individuals have lived together throughout their childhood, the more likely they are to be related (Lieberman et al., 2007).

Much of the evidence for maternal-perinatal association and co-residence duration as cues of kinship come from a peculiar source: incest aversions. It has been known for some time that reproduction among very close relatives, known as *inbreeding*, can have detrimental consequences for offspring primarily because of the increased likelihood of inheriting recessive genes (genes that are only expressed when there are two copies, one inherited from each parent) that have detrimental effects. As inbreeding among close relatives is deleterious, organisms should have evolved to avoid it by using kin recognition mechanisms to determine which individuals are appropriate mates and which ones—like siblings—are not. The result is "incest aversion," which is an aversion to mating with close relatives.

Numerous studies of real-world populations show that people tend to avoid marrying and reproducing with others that they were reared with, *even if they are not actually related*. In Israel, for example, there exist communities known as *kibbutzim*, where children were often reared together, irrespective of whether they were siblings. As the children grow older, they learn that they are not necessarily related to the other children. Nonetheless, when they reach adulthood and get married, they virtually never marry someone from the same *kibbutz* (Shepher, 1971; Talmon, 1964). This suggests that humans use co-residence as a kinship cue.

More evidence of this comes from studies of "minor" marriages in Taiwan. In such marriages, a family would adopt a child into their family in order to rear it as a future bride or groom for their own children. As it turns out, the longer the adopted child lived with his or her future wife or husband, the more likely they were to divorce and the fewer children they were likely to produce together (Lieberman, 2009; Wolf, 1993). However, because the older children could also use maternal-perinatal association as a kinship cue, co-residence duration predicts divorce and the reproductive behaviour only of the younger individual in the married couple; the older member of the pair is averse to the marital union irrespective of how long the two lived together (Lieberman, 2009).

Maternal-perinatal association trumps co-residence duration in other studies as well. For instance, university students were asked about their aversions to sexual intercourse between a pair of hypothetical siblings (not their own). Among those who only had older opposite-sex siblings, co-residence duration predicted their aversion to incest among the hypothetical siblings. Those who only had younger opposite-sex siblings, however, were averse to the situation in general, and co-residence duration did not further predict aversion (Lieberman et al., 2007).

Maternal-perinatal association and co-residence duration are good cues that others are one's siblings, but how does one recognize other relatives? Moreover, how can we be sure that our sibling is a full sibling (that is, we share both the same mother and father) or is only a half-sibling (sharing only one parent in common)? Likewise, how can a man know that the child his mate just delivered is in fact his own, and not the offspring of some other man?

A solution to this may have to do with **phenotypic similarity** or physical resemblance. The more genetically close two individuals are, the more they will tend to resemble one another. Think of monozygotic ("identical") twins, dizygotic ("fraternal") twins, and full siblings. The relatedness of monozygotic twins is greater than the relatedness of dizygotic twins or full siblings, as the former share all their genes in common (so $r = 1$), whereas the latter share only half of their genes on average (so $r = 0.5$). Monozygotic twins are nicknamed "identical" twins for a reason: they usually appear much more similar to one another than do other kinds of sibling pairs. The same goes for decreasing degrees of relatedness: organisms will tend to resemble their genetic parents and siblings more than their grandparents, aunts, uncles, and cousins, but will still tend to resemble these individuals more than others who are even less related (or unrelated).

Phenotypic similarity is caused by shared genes—the more genetically similar two individuals are, the more phenotypically similar they will tend to be—as well as shared environment. As individuals who are more genetically similar will be raised under similar circumstances (e.g., reared by the same parents, share the same diet, etc.), there will be both genetic and environmental influences on physical resemblance, such as in the shape of one's face or their odour. Recent evidence suggests that people can accurately judge the relatedness of strangers (Kaminski, Dridi, Graff, & Gentaz, 2009) and that they do so in large part based on the apparent similarity of those individuals (DeBruine, Smith, Jones, Roberts, Petrie, & Spector, 2009; Maloney, & Dal Martello, 2006). Moreover, participants trust and cooperate more with face images manipulated to resemble their own faces than with faces that have not been manipulated to be self-resembling (DeBruine, 2002; Krupp, DeBruine, & Barclay, 2008). And, as expected, participants also find self-resembling *opposite-sex* faces less sexually attractive than non-resembling faces (DeBruine, 2005; DeBruine, Jones, Watkins, Roberts, Little, Smith, & Quist, 2011).

It seems likely, then, that people use phenotypic similarity to inform their decisions about how much they ought to cooperate with, or invest in, another person. Although men and woman seem equally swayed by the facial resemblance of children to themselves (Bressan, Bertamini, Nalli, & Zanutto, 2009; DeBruine, 2004), men's investment in his putative offspring is a function of how much those offspring resemble him (Alvergne, Faurie, & Raymond, 2009; Apicella, & Marlowe, 2004). More research is needed to understand how kin recognition informs our day to day decisions, but it appears that everything from mate choice to parenting to interactions with complete strangers are affected by psychological mechanisms designed by natural selection to assess genetic relatedness.

TABLE #2.6	Inclusive fitness is a measure of the success of genes in promoting social behaviour by being able to use this behaviour to promote copies of itself in others

Inclusive Fitness & Behaviour	Kin Recognition
• **Inclusive fitness** is a way of understanding social behaviour in humans and other species i.e. eusocial species • Inclusive fitness has relevance in social dynamics such as homicide – it predicts why we are increasingly likely to kill those that are decreasingly related to us • Inclusive fitness also predicts nepotism, the increased willingness to help or save those increasingly related to us in serious and/or life threatening situations	• Important to inclusive fitness is **kin recognition** – the ability to implicitly or explicitly be aware of who our relatives are • A number of cues aid in this such as **maternal-perinatal association** for mothers and their offspring, as well as **co-residence duration** • Evidence also exists as seen through the phenomenon of incest avoidance because of inbreeding's harmful genetic effects • Another cue used, especially for other relatives that do not co-reside etc., is **phenotypic resemblance** or physical and behavioural similarity • All cues are used in some combination or other to inform decisions about co-operation and investment, as well as mate choice, parenting, and interactions with non-relatives

Parent-Offspring Conflict

Competition for Resources

From a Darwinian perspective, parent-offspring solidarity at first sounds like a no-brainer. The primary way in which organisms contribute to the replication of their genes is by producing and rearing young who will reproduce in their turn. If the psychology of parenthood has been shaped by natural selection, we should therefore expect parents to cherish their young, and to invest time and energy in ensuring their welfare, which of course they do.

But that's not the whole story, as Robert Trivers (1971) explained in an influential theoretical analysis of "parent-offspring conflict". Such conflict is inescapable in sexually reproducing species, Trivers argued, because parent and offspring are not genetically identical, with the result that the policy that would maximize parental fitness typically differs from the policy that would maximize offspring fitness.

Suppose that you have a sister. From *your* perspective, you are twice as "valuable", in the currency that natural selection tends to maximize, as your sister. Why? Because any child that you eventually produce will have twice as many of your genes and will contribute twice as much to your inclusive fitness as would your sister's child -- your niece or nephew. The trouble is that your sister sees things differently: from *her* perspective, she's twice as valuable as your. And from your *mother's* perspective, you and your sister are *equally* valuable (if you're of equally good "quality" and hence reproductive potential). She just wishes you weren't so *selfish* in your dealings with each other!

Just to be sure you've got the point, consider the following imaginary numerical example. Suppose that a mother owl has two little owlets in her nest, who are identical in age, condition, and quality, and hence in their statistical expectation of future reproduction. Suppose further that the mother has brought two rodents, which are not readily divisible, home to feed to her brood, that eating one rodent would increase either owlet's expected future reproduction by an arbitrary 4 "fitness units" and that gulping down both rodents would give either owlet à 7 "fitness unit" gain. What should the mother do?

There are three possible allocations: owlet A gets both rodents, owlet B gets both, or each get one. The fitness consequences are laid out in the little table below. From mother's perspective, if either owlet monopolizes the food, there will be a total gain in her brood's fitness of 7 units, and since she is a 0.5 relative to her offspring, that's a 3.5 unit gain for her fitness. But if she divides the food between the young, the brood's total fitness, and hence her own, will be a little higher still, so natural selection may have inclined her to treat her young equitably.

	Mother's Fitness	Owlet A's Fitness	Owlet B's Fitness
Owlet A gets 2	7*0.5 = 3.5	7	7*0.5 = 3.5
Owlet B gets 2	7*0.5 = 3.5	7*0.5 = 3.5	7
Each gets 1	(4+4)*0.5 = 4	4+(4*0.5) = 6	4+(4*0.5) = 6

Each owlet, by contrast, would do best by monopolizing the food, if it could, even though food eaten by one's sibling has a positive impact on one's own inclusive fitness, thanks to kinship. The trouble is that that positive impact is discounted by the degree of relatedness between the siblings of $r = 0.5$. And of course, that's assuming that they are full siblings, with the same father as well as the same mother. If the owlets are instead only half siblings, with different fathers, then the fitness value to either owlet of an increase in its sibling's expected reproduction must be discounted even more, with the result that the youngsters' inclinations to monopolize the prize should be intensified, according to the revised incentive structure below.

TABLE #2.7

	Mother's Fitness	Owlet A's Fitness	Owlet B's Fitness
Owlet A gets 2	7*0.5 = 3.5	7	7*0.25 = 1.75
Owlet B gets 2	7*0.5 = 3.5	7*0.25 = 1.75	7
Each gets 1	(4+4)*0.5 = 4	4+(4*0.25) = 5	4+(4*0.25) = 5

That, in a nutshell, is the logic of parent-offspring conflict. In a sense, it is a consequence of sibling conflict, and the logic applies just as well to competition with future siblings who have not yet been born: from my mother's perspective, any future young that she has will be as closely related to her as I am, but they won't be as closely related to me as I am, so I should have evolved to place less value on them, relative to myself, than mom does.

Draft

The numbers in the owlet example are imaginary, but they are not totally arbitrary. You may have noticed that eating successive rodents yields *diminishing marginal gains* – an owlet gets less benefit from the second one (3 fitness units) than from the first (4 units). This is essential if the theory is to work - if there were linear gains, mother would have no incentive to divide the goodies, and if the gains were actually *increasing*, her best strategy would be to feed everything to one chick and let the other starve, But diminishing marginal gains is actually the typical state of affairs in nature. (Think about your own capacity to convert a second burger, or a third or fourth, into growth and survival increments!).

An Evolutionary Arms Race

What Trivers's theory tells us is that natural selection acts on dependent young in such a way as to make them seek a little bit larger share of parentally controlled resources than the parent is selected to provide. In the parlance of genetics, we can say that genes expressed in offspring are selected to extract more parental resource than is optimal for parental fitness. Moreover, this situation engenders selection favouring genes which, when expressed in parental tissues, will counter the effects of the recently selected genes expressed in offspring, a state of affairs which can lead to an "evolutionary arms race". In other words, a mutation in a gene expressed in offspring that helps the youngster extract more maternal resource than is optimal for mom may rapidly increase in prevalence, but this creates a situation in which a gene that has a contrary effect when expressed in the mother can also spread to fixation. Thus, for example, over evolutionary time, young may increasingly exaggerate their "needs" through louder begging, while mothers evolve to discount the escalating signal. Such a process can be very wasteful: after several steps in such an "arms race", parental food delivery may remain right where it began, while begging has become more energetically expensive and perhaps even risky, insofar as it reveals the young's whereabouts to predators.

Interesting in principle, you may be thinking, but have such evolutionary arms races really taken place and left their mark on psychology, physiology, and behaviour? Well, think about what happens when young are weaned. In human beings and many other mammals, nursing young object when their mother decides to cut off the milk and redirect her accumulated energy towards the production of the next baby. Young who are being weaned often scream and pester their mothers mercilessly; the mothers in their turn may assault their own young to get them to desist. This is a conflict that imposes real costs on both parties, and without the insight provided by Trivers's theory, we would have no explanation for why it exists. If mother and young had a unity of interests, wouldn't selection have favoured a more harmonious transition?

Where parent-offspring conflict theory has proven most fruitful is in the analysis of interactions prior to birth. Maternal-fetal interactions are extremely complex

---

62

and differ remarkably from one species to the next. Recently, thanks especially to the insights of Harvard biologist David Haig (1993, 1996, 2010), the functional significance of many previously puzzling phenomena in mammalian pregnancy has been illuminated, including why fetuses secrete massive amounts of substances (chorionic gonadotrophins and placental lactogens) that are evolutionarily modified derivatives of maternal hormones and that act on maternal hormone receptors in potentially dangerous ways while serving no essential function (Haig 1993).

Indeed, the very fact that the physiology of maternal-fetal interaction is so much more variable across species than is the case with other organ systems is explained by parent-offspring conflict theory. Maternal-fetal interaction is unstable because of the dynamics of evolutionary arms races, described above, in which the fixation of each novel maternal or fetal adaptation creates a selection pressure on the other party to evolve counter-adaptations. It follows that this is an area where endocrine and other mechanisms evolve rapidly, without necessarily improving global performance, and different lineages diverge as a result of their idiosyncratic sequences of mutation.

SECTION REVIEW: Parent-Offspring Conflict

TABLE #2.8	**Parent-Offspring Conflict occurs and it too can be understood as a function of natural selection**	
	Competition for Resources	**An Evolutionary Arms Race**
	• Differential fitness results can occur depending on parental investment; siblings each feel entitled to the majority of parental resources	• Such competition for fitness results in an evolutionary arms race among parents and offspring although it can be quite costly and risky for fitness in the end
	• Offspring often seek more resources than parents can provide and is optimal for parental fitness	• Pre-natal conflict provides the best evidence for this
	• The best strategy for parents is to divide resources equally among offspring, but the best strategy for offspring is to fight for the most resources	• Fetuses secrete substances that act on maternal hormone receptors in a dangerous fashion, yet the adaptive purpose of this is unclear or non-existent

Concluding Thoughts

In this chapter, we have illustrated the approach taken by evolutionary psychologists with a few particular examples, some of which have attracted a lot of recent research attention. But if the human brain and mind have indeed evolved under the influence of selection - and there is no scientific controversy about this point - then evolutionary biology's relevance for psychologists must be much broader than these few examples.

Psychologists have studied basic motives like hunger and fear, for example, for decades, and they have made great progress in understanding the underlying "machinery", arguably because they have approached these topics with sound adaptationist hypotheses about what hunger and fear are organized to achieve. But the first-pass adaptationist hypotheses that the motivational system of hunger is organized to acquire needed calories and the motivational system of fear is organized to avoid dangers are insufficient. What explicit evolutionary thought adds is the recognition that acquiring calories and avoiding harms are not ends in themselves but are means to the end of fitness, and may be overridden. Thus, for example, hens who are incubating eggs in a nest and who cannot leave the nest without exposing the eggs to predation risk experience an adoptive anorexia and programmed weight loss during the incubation period. The motivation to feed is not simply a response to current energy levels, but is modulated in relation to other aspects of a more encompassing fitness-promoting behavioural "strategy". Similarly, parental fish will approach a predator more bravely when they have helpless young in the nest who would be consumed if that predator were not driven off. Thus, fear, too, is not simply a response to dangers to one's own life, but is again modulated as a component of more encompassing "strategies". We suggest that the analysis of any motivational system is likely to be incomplete until the researchers' adaptationism is informed by explicit selectionism.

Personality psychology needs evolutionary theory: the very question of why there is so much diversity in personality traits (which are largely heritable) demands an analysis in terms of natural selection. Abnormal psychology needs evolutionary theory: we cannot even recognize pathologies with confidence until we understand what attributes (perhaps including nasty attributes like the capacity for violence) are adaptations. In short, we maintain that all of psychology can and eventually will profit from explicitly Darwinian analysis. We hope that the examples developed in this chapter will inspire our readers to at least pay some thought to this proposition.

References

Alvergne, A., Faurie, C., & Raymond, M. (2009). Father-offspring resemblance predicts paternal investment in humans. *Animal Behaviour, 78,* 61-69.

Apicella, C. L., & Marlowe, F. W. (2004). Perceived mate fidelity and paternal resemblance predict men's investment in children. *Evolution and Human Behavior, 25,* 371-378.

Bressan, P., Bertamini, M., Nalli, A., & Zanutto, A. (2009). Men do not have a stronger preference than women for self-resemblant child faces. *Archives of Sexual Behavior, 38,* 657-664.

Bowles, S., & Posel, D. (2005). Genetic relatedness predicts South African migrant workers' remittances to their families. *Nature, 434,* 380-383.

Burnstein, E., Crandall, C., & Kitayama, S. (1994). Some neo-Darwinian decision rules for altruism: Weighing cues for inclusive fitness as a function of the biological importance of the decision. *Journal of Personality and Social Psychology, 67,* 773-789.

Buss, D. M. (1989). Sex differences in human mate preferences: Evolutionary hypotheses tested in 37 cultures. *Behavioral and Brain Sciences, 12,* 1-49.

Buss, D. M., Larsen, R. J., Westen, D., & Semmelroth, J. (1992). Sex differences in jealousy: Evolution, physiology, and psychology. *Psychological Science, 3,* 251-255.

Buss, D. M., & Schmidt, D. P. (1993). Sexual strategies theory: An evolutionary perspective on human mating. *Psychological Review, 100,* 204-232.

Buunk, B. P., Angleitner, A., Oubaid, V., & Buss, D. M. (1996). Sex differences in jealousy in evolutionary and cultural perspective: Tests from the Netherlands, Germany, and the United States. *Psychological Science,7,* 359-363.

Clark, R. D., III., & Hatfield, E. (1989). Gender differences in receptivity to sexual offers. *Journal of Psychology & Human Sexuality, 2,* 39-55.

Clutton-Brock, T. H., & Parker, G. A. (1992). Potential reproductive rates and the operation of sexual selection. *Quarterly Review of Biology, 67,* 437-456.

Cousyn, C., De Meester, L., Colbourne, J. K., Brendonck, L., Verschuren, D., & Volckaert, F. (2001). Rapid, local adaptation of zooplankton behavior to changes in predation pressure in the absence of neutral genetic changes. *Proceedings of the National Academy of Sciences, 98,* 6256-6260.

Daly, M., & Wilson, M. (1988). *Homicide.* Hawthorne, NY: Aldine de Gruyter.

Daly, M., Wilson, M., & Weghorst, S. J. (1982). *Ethology & Sociobiology, 3,* 11-27.

DeBruine, L. M. (2002). Facial resemblance enhances trust. *Proceedings of the Royal Society, Series B: Biological Sciences, 269,* 1307-1312.

DeBruine, L. M. (2004). Resemblance to self increases the appeal of child faces to both men and women. *Evolution and Human Behavior, 25,* 142-154.

DeBruine, L. M. (2005). Trustworthy but not lust-worthy: Context-specific effects of facial resemblance. *Proceedings of the Royal Society, Series B: Biological Sciences, 272,* 919-922.

DeBruine, L. M., Jones, B. C., Watkins, C. D., Roberts, S. C., Little, A. C., Smith, F. G., & Quist, M. C. (2011). Opposite-sex siblings decrease attraction, but not prosocial attributions, to self-resembling opposite-sex faces. *Proceedings of the National Academy of Science, 108,* 11710-11714.

DeBruine, L. M., Smith, F. G., Jones, B. C., Roberts, S. C., Petrie, M., & Spector, T. D. (2009). Kin recognition signals in adult faces. *Vision Research, 49,* 38-43.

De Meester, L. (1993). Genotype, fish-mediated chemicals, and phototactic behavior in Daphnia Magna. *Ecology, 74,* 1467-1474.

Flinn, M. V. (1988). Mate guarding in a caribbean village. *Ethology & Sociobiology, 9,*1-28.

Frank, S. A. (1998). *Foundations of social evolution.* Princeton, NJ: Princeton University Press.

Gangestad, S.W., Simpson, J.A., Cousins, A.J., Garver-Apgar, C.E., & Christensen, P.N. (2004). Women's preferences for male behavioral displays change across the menstrual cycle. *Psychological Science, 15,* 203–207.

Gangestad, S. W., & Thornhill, R. (2008). Human oestrus. *Proceedings of the Royal Society, Series B: Biological Sciences, 275,* 991-1000.

Grant, P.R. (1991) Natural selection and Darwin's finches. *Scientific American* (Oct).

Grant, P.R. & Grant, B.R. (2006) Evolution of character displacement in Darwin's finches. *Science* 313 : 224-226.

Haig, D. (1993). Genetic conflicts in human pregnancy. *Quarterly Review of Biology, 68,* 495-532.

Haig, D. (1996). Placental hormones, genomic imprinting, and maternal-fetal communication. *Journal of Evolutionary Biology, 9,* 357-380.

Haig, D. (2010) Transfers and transitions: parent-offspring conflict, genomic imprinting, and the evolution of human life history. *Proceedings of the National Academy of Sciences, 197,* 1731-1735.

Hames, R. (1987). Garden labor exchange among the Ye'kwana. *Ethology and Sociobiology, 8,* 259-284.

Hamilton, W. D. (1963). The evolution of altruistic behavior. *American Naturalist, 97,* 354-356.

Haselton, M.G., & Miller, G.F. (2006). Evidence for ovulatory shifts in attraction to artistic and entrepreneurial excellence. *Human Nature, 17,* 50-73.

Havlicek, J. & Roberts, S.C. (2009) MHC-correlated mate choice in humans: a review. *Psychoneuroendocrinology* 34: 497-512.

Hughes, W. O. H., Oldroyd, B. P., Beekman, M., & Ratnieks, F. L. W. (2008). Ancestral monogamy shows kin selection is key to the evolution of eusociality. *Science, 320,* 1213-1216.

Jackson, R. E., & Cormack, L. K. (2008). Evolved navigation theory and the environmental vertical illusion. *Evolution and Human Behavior, 29,* 299-304.

Jasienska, G., Ziomkiewicz, A., Ellison, P. T., Lipson, S. F., & Thune, I. (2004). Large breasts and narrow waists indicate high reproductive potential in women. *Proceedings of the Royal Society, Series B: Biological Sciences, 271,* 1213-1217.

Johnston, V. S., Hagel, R., Franklin, M., Fink, B., & Grammer, K. (2001). Male facial attractiveness: Evidence for hormone mediated adaptive design. *Evolution and Human Behavior, 23,* 251–267.

Jones, B. C., Little, A. C., Penton-Voak, I. S., Tiddeman, B. P., Burt, D. M., & Perrett, D. I. (2001). Facial symmetry and judgements of apparent health: Support for a "good genes" explanation of the attractiveness—symmetry relationship. *Evolution and Human Behavior, 22,* 417-429.

Kaminski, G., Dridi, S., Graff, C., & Gentaz, E. (2009). Human ability to detect kinship in strangers' faces: effects of the degree of relatedness. *Proceedings of the Royal Society, Series B: Biological Sciences, 276,* 3193-3200.

Krupp, D. B., DeBruine, L. M., & Barclay, P. (2008). A cue of kinship promotes cooperation for the public good. *Evolution and Human Behavior, 29,* 49-55.

Langlois, J. H., & Roggman, L. A. (1990). Attractive faces are only average. *Psychological Science, 1,* 115-121.

Lieberman, D., Tooby, J., & Cosmides, L. (2007). The architecture of human kin detection. *Nature, 445,* 727-731.

Lieberman, D. (2009). Rethinking the Taiwanese minor marriage data: evidence the mind uses multiple kinship cues to regulate inbreeding avoidance. *Evolution and Human Behavior, 30,* 153-160.

Little, A. C., & Jones, B. C. (2003). Evidence against perceptual bias views for symmetry preferences in human faces. *Proceedings of the Royal Society, Series B: Biological Sciences, 270,* 1759-1763.

Maloney, L. T., & Dal Martello, M. F. (2006). Kin recognition and the perceived facial similarity of children. *Journal of Vision, 6,* 1047-1056.

Penn, D.J., Damjanovich, K. & Potts, W.K. (2002) MHC heterozygosity confers a selective advantage against multiple-strain infections. *Proceedings of the National Academy of Sciences, U.S.A.* 99: 11260-11264.

Penton-Voak, I. S, Jones, B. C, Little, A. C, Baker, S., Tiddeman, B., Burt, D. M, & Perrett, D. I. (2001). Symmetry, sexual dimorphism in facial proportions, and male facial attractiveness. *Proceedings of the Royal Society, Series B: Biological Sciences, 268,* 1617–1623.

Penton-Voak, I. S., Perrett, D. I., Castles, D. L., Kobayashi, T., Burt, D. M., Murray, L. K., et al. (1999). Menstrual cycle alters face preference. *Nature, 399,* 741-742.

Perrett, D. I., Burt, D. M, Penton-Voak, I. S., Lee, K. J., Rowland, D. A., & Edwards, R. (1999). Symmetry and human facial attractiveness. *Evolution and Human Behavior, 20,* 295–307.

Scheib, J. E., Gangestad, S. W., & Thornhill, R. (1999). Facial attractiveness, symmetry, and cues to good genes. *Proceedings of the Royal Society, Series B: Biological Sciences, 266,* 1913–1917.

Shepher, J. (1971). Mate selection among second generation kibbutz adolescents and adults: Incest avoidance and negative imprinting. *Archives of Sexual Behavior, 1,* 293-307.

Queller, D. C., & Strassmann, J. E. (1998). Kin selection and social insects. *Bioscience, 48,* 165-175.

Sclomer, G. L., del Giudice, M., & Ellis, B. J. (2011). Parent-offspring conflict theory: an evolutionary framework for understanding conflict within

Draft

human families. *Psychological Review, xx*, xxx-xxx.

Stewart-Williams, S. (2007). Altruism among kin vs. nonkin: effects of cost of help and reciprocal exchange. *Evolution and Human Behavior, 28*, 193-198.

Talmon, Y. (1964). Mate selection in collective settlements. *American Sociological Review, 29*, 491-508.

Thornhill, R., & Gangestad, S. W. (1999). The scent of symmetry: A human sex pheromone that signals fitness? *Evolution and Human Behavior, 20*, 175-201.

Trivers, R. L. (1972). Parental investment and sexual selection. In B. Campbell (Ed.), *Sexual selection and the descent of man* (pp. 136-179). Chicago: Aldine.

Trivers, R. L. (1974). Parent-offspring conflict. *American Zoologist, 14*, 249-264.

Wedekind, C., Seebeck, T., Bettens, F. & Paepke, A.J. (1995) MHC-dependent mate preferences in humans. *Proceedings of the Royal Society of London: Biological Sciences* 260: 245-249.

Weiner, J. (1994) *The beak of the finch.* NY: Knopf.

Wilson, M., & Daly, M. (1992). The man who mistook his wife for a chattel. In J. H. Barkow, L. Cosmides & J. Tooby (Eds.), *The adapted mind* (pp. 289-322). New York: Oxford University Press.

Wolf, A. P. (1993). Westermarck redivivus. *Annual Review of Anthropology, 22*, 157-175.

Chapter

3

Neuroscience

The next major level we will study is Neuroscience. Everything you have ever thought, remembered, or perceived involved, at some point, a series of electrochemical events in the central nervous system. This has some profound implications; one being that it means you have no *direct experience* of the world around you. When you 'experience' the warmth of the sun, or the feel of grass on your bare feet, you are not actually *experiencing* the warmth or the grass, you are *experiencing* a series of events in your central nervous system, which were set in motion by the actual stimuli in the environment. In other words, in order for you to become aware of anything out there in the world, the world has to induce a certain pattern of activity in the brain, and it is this activity that we actually become 'aware' of, not the world itself. These electrochemical processes will always be 'in between' your awareness and the outside world. This may seem like a pretty fine point, but it has been the subject of much philosophical discussion. For our purposes, the important point is the fundamental importance of the physiological activity of the brain and its component parts in human thought and behaviour.

Psychologists have been studying the human brain for just over a century, although anatomical and medical studies go back somewhat further. Our modern investigations of the brain have generally followed one of two lines of questioning, and, as we shall see, each does a great deal to inform the other. The first, and to a large extent easier, type of questions asked were *structural* questions: What was the brain made of? How is it constructed? Where are all the different bits and how are they connected to each other? Answering these questions can give us a 'map' or 'blueprint' of the brain's architecture. While much work has been done in this area, and we have a pretty good general idea of what brains look like, it should be noted that advances in technology continue to allow us to answer these kinds of questions in more and more detail. As useful as this information continues to be, we clearly need other kinds of information as well. Imagine you were trying to figure out how an automobile worked. Knowing where all the parts were, what they were made of, and how they were connected (i.e., the structure of the car and its various parts) is certainly part of the answer, but it is equally critical that you

70

Draft

learn what all those parts <u>do</u>. If you don't know what the radiator <u>does</u>, you will probably never understand <u>why</u> it is connected to the rest of the car the way it is, and how that helps the car to function. That is, you will also need *functional* information if you are to understand the whole picture. In our discussions of the brain and its various activities, we will refer to both structural and functional aspects of the brain. Any hope of understanding this organ clearly requires both kinds of information.

The human brain is an extremely complex structure. The brain and the spinal cord, both encased in bone, make up our *central nervous system* (CNS). All the remaining nerve tissue in the body constitutes the *peripheral nervous system* (PNS). Considering its importance, the brain is not very large. It typically weighs between 3.0 and 3.5 pounds, making up about 2% of our total body weight. It does, however, consume a disproportionate amount of the body's energy supply, burning roughly 20% of our oxygen intake when we are at rest.

There are two basic types of cell in the brain: *glial* cells and *neurons*. In general, *glial cells* provide structure and perform various 'housekeeping' tasks in the brain. Note that this description may be very simplified and somewhat naïve, as we are learning more about glial cells all the time, and they may do a lot more than housekeeping. You will, in fact, meet a couple of highly specialized types of glial cells in the discussion of neural transmission in the lectures. The second type of cell, *the neuron*, has certainly received a lot more attention. This is the type of cell typically referred to as a 'brain cell' in the popular media. While glial cells actually outnumber neurons in the brain by a fairly large margin, there are still about 100 billion neurons in the average adult human brain, and it is the neurons that seem to be performing all the more interesting functions. Further, each of these 100 billion neurons may form synapses (i.e., connections) to thousands of other neurons, resulting in a brain with about 1,000,000,000,000,000 (a thousand *trillion*) different connections. You can see why it is considered a complex organ.

You should also note that we seem to have run into the reductionism problem again: Despite the fact that it may be entirely accurate, how can we expect to give or understand explanations of altruism, social phobias, drug addiction, or any other aspects of human behaviour in terms of the activity of 100 billion neurons? Further, as we shall see, neurons themselves are hardly the most basic possible level of explanation. Each of those neurons contains a variety of structures and *organelles* (i.e., little bits of biological machinery inside the cell that perform some function), and each of these is composed of various molecules, etc… At some point, our explanations become so accurate they are useless. For these reasons, psychologists examine the brain at a number of different 'levels', and in this section of the course you will see the structure and function of the brain from a variety of perspectives. You will learn the basic, large scale anatomy of the brain, discuss the structure and function of various specialized systems, and also look at the neuron itself and how it does what it does.

Consciousness and awareness

Our widespread belief that our mind is somehow separate from our physical nature perhaps arises from what seem like irreconcilable differences between things like thoughts, memories, and sensations, and the physical operation of our bodies. How can we imagine that the ineffable beauty of a musical composition is actually the result of some pattern of activity in our cells? The first philosopher to seriously discuss the mind-body problem was Rene Descartes (1596-1650 - you may have also encountered another of his developments, the Cartesian coordinate system, in your study of mathematics). Descartes was a *dualist* - he suggested that the body was like a machine that followed the laws of physics, and was distinct from the mind, which was a non-physical entity that did not follow physical laws. He believed that the seat of the soul was in the pineal gland (the actual operation of which we will study later) and it somehow affected control of the body through the nerves. These ideas set the stage for philosophical discussion of the mind-body problem that continues today. The more important result, however, was that these ideas encouraged others to investigate exactly how the body does operate, and the sciences of neurobiology and neuropsychology, which developed from these investigations, have been increasingly successful at explaining mental phenomena. There have not, as of yet, been any successful challenges of the fundamental idea that it is impossible for the mental state of a person to change without some physical change in his brain.

Epilepsy and the Split Brain

One interesting demonstration of the relationship between consciousness, awareness, and the underlying physical structure of the brain is found by studying the behaviour of patients who have undergone a surgical procedure for the treatment of epilepsy. Epilepsy is a chronic disorder characterized by recurring seizures caused by abnormal activity in the brain. Before the advent of more modern medical treatments for epilepsy, very little could be done for a person with "falling sickness" (as it was known in the middle ages) and in fact the person with this illness would likely be subjected to various superstitious remedies such as spells, amulets and even exorcisms. Today, most individuals can be made completely seizure-free with modern drug therapy. There remains a minority (20%) of patients who are not helped by drugs, but these cases may still be helped by epilepsy surgery. Modern surgical techniques target the exact site in the brain where the seizure originates, but epilepsy surgery has a long history, dating back as early as 1886. One fairly radical surgical procedure that was used a number of times during the 1950s and 60s was split-brain surgery. In patients with very severe epilepsy, seizure-causing activity begins in one hemisphere of the brain and then quickly spreads to the other hemisphere over the *corpus callosum*, a bundle of nerve fibers near the centre of the brain connecting the two sides. Once the whole brain becomes involved the seizure can be very severe, so in some patients *corpus callosotomies* were performed, severing some or all of these nerve fibres in order to reduce the severity of the seizure. This procedure was found to have some important adverse effects on the brain's normal function so after the 1960's very few of these procedures were performed. From the patients' perspective this procedure may not have been ideal, but for the purposes of understanding something about how the brain operates, scientists gained a great deal of very important information. Experiments performed on split-brain patients revealed information about *hemispheric specialization* - the principle that different sides of the brain perform different functions. If a patient with a split brain were shown an image to his left visual field (which projects to the right side of the brain exclusively), he would be unable to name what he saw, since the left side of the brain controls the function of speech. Similarly if an image of an object, say a key, was shown to the right visual field (and thus the left side of the brain), the patient would be able to name the object but would not be able to pick up a similar object from in front of them using their left hand, since the left hand is controlled by the right side of the brain. In some patients the two sides of the brain seemed to take on almost completely independent existences. One split-brain patient, an accountant, was asked to write out what he would like to do for a living - with his right hand he wrote "accountant" and with his left hand he wrote "racing driver"! These experiments were important in revealing the extent to which functions are localized to specific areas in the brain, and many neuroscience experiments continue to be conducted in order to refine our understanding of the localization of function. It is also suggested that consciousness and awareness are intimately tied to the underlying structure of the brain.

Divisions of the Nervous System - The Central and Peripheral Nervous Systems

As mentioned, the nervous system can be roughly divided into two parts. The *central nervous system* (CNS) consists of the brain and the spinal cord, the part of the nervous system encased in bone. The brain is contained within the skull and the spinal cord is encased within the vertebral column. The brain, weighing about 1.3 kg in an adult, is a large mass of cells known as neurons - about 100 billion of them - as well as many more supporting cells known as glia. We will discuss the function of these cells in more detail later. Once the nerve fibers leave the bony protection they become part of the *peripheral nervous system*, the collection of nerves and peripheral ganglia (ganglia are small groups of neuron cell bodies) located outside of the CNS. Fibers that carry information outward from the central nervous system to the periphery of the body are known as efferent nerve fibers. Fibers that carry information inward to the central nervous system from the periphery of the body are known as afferent nerve fibers.

The Somatic and Autonomic Nervous Systems

The peripheral nervous system can actually be divided again into two parts, this time according to their function. The part that receives sensory information from the sensory organs (eyes, ears, sense of touch etc) and controls the voluntary movements of the muscles is called the *somatic nervous system*. This is the part that brings us information that we are consciously aware of, and allows us to perform actions under conscious control. Another part of the peripheral nervous system, the *autonomic nervous system*, controls the things that happen outside of our conscious awareness and control. This system regulates the smooth muscles, the cardiac muscle, and allows for the glands to operate. Smooth muscle causes certain organs to contract, such as the blood vessels, the pupil of the eye, the gastrointestinal tract and the uterus. The autonomic system can be divided yet again into two systems. The *sympathetic division* of the autonomic nervous system is involved with preparing the body for emergencies - the so-called "fight or flight" response. The result of stimulation by this system is an increase in heart rate, a dilation of the pupils, dilation of the internal structures of the lungs, inhibition of digestion and an inhibition of the contraction of the bladder and the rectum. These results are quite general - one of them cannot happen in the absence of all of the others, as the nerves of the sympathetic system branch quite widely to reach a number of organs simultaneously, and because this system also causes the release of adrenaline from the adrenal gland into the blood, ensuring that the response reaches organs that are not directly connected to the nerves.

The *parasympathetic system* is almost the opposite in nature to the sympathetic system. Its activation begins a cascade of events including a slowing of the heart, a lowering of blood pressure, a contraction of the pupils, increase in activity in the gastrointestinal tract, and secretion of digestive juices. These are all responses that return body functions to normal after activation of the sympathetic system, and generally conserve and increase the body's energy resources.

The Nerve Cell and the Action Potential

The Neuron

The most important elementary unit in your nervous system is the neuron. All animals (including humans) are *eukaryotes*, meaning that the cells in our bodies have a fairly complex internal structure, consisting of a number of elements having distinct roles in its operation. There are several hundred different types of cells in the human body, and all of these cells have many of these elements (known as *organelles*) in common - each cell has a cell body or *soma* that is surrounded by a membrane separating it from the other cells, within which can be found a nucleus containing the DNA that regulates much of the cells operation, and various other membrane-bound organelles such as *mitochondria* and *ribosomes*. These organelles act as chemical factories, responsible for synthesizing the various substances needed for the operation of the cell. In addition to their common elements, each of these cell types is specialized for performing some unique function within the body. The neuron is a cell that specializes in integrating and communicating information, and has a number of special adaptations that allow it to process and transmit information via electrical and chemical signals. Our 100 billion neurons are contained in a volume of around 1400ml in our brain. Although the brain contains only about 2% of our body mass, it consumes 20% of the calories we expend, and the vast majority of this energy is expended on the energetic needs of the neurons.

STRUCTURE OF THE NEURON

Although there are many different subtypes of neurons, most neurons are arranged in a similar fashion, having special structures called *dendrites* dedicated to receiving and integrating incoming information, and other structures called *axons* dedicated to passing this information on to other cells. In a typical neuron a number of branching dendrites converge at the cell body, receiving impulses from many other neurons, and bring them all together at the cell body. Usually one axon exits the cell body and can extend for long distances, even the entire length of the spinal cord, and may branch multiple times to carry the neuron's impulses to multiple destinations. At the end of the axon, the destination of the neuron's impulse might be another neuron, or some other sort of cell such as a muscle or gland that is capable of receiving and responding to a nerve impulse - these cells are known as *effectors*. Thus a sequence of activity or information flow occurs, from the dendrites where information is gathered, to the cell body where the information from all the multiple dendrites is integrated. The activity then flows down along the axon to other neurons where complex calculations can occur, or to effector cells, where the information is acted upon, perhaps making your heart beat, your arm move, or your salivary glands secrete saliva.

THE DENDRITE

The branched projections that conduct the nerve impulses received from other cells to the cell body are usually fairly short, extending only a few hundred microns away from the cell. They are covered in tiny spines and on these spines the connections from the axons of other neurons are made at a junction known as a *synapse*. The synapse is the gap across which the stimulation from one neuron must cross in order to affect another. Some neuron types have up to 200,000 of these synapses, although 1000-10,000 synapses per neuron is more typical. We will delve into the operation of these synapses in a later section. For our present purpose, it is important to know that the dendrites bring together the impulses occurring across the many thousands of synapses to their final destination at the cell body.

THE CELL BODY

The cell body or soma of a neuron in a human is quite small, typically ranging from 4 microns for the smallest type of neuron (the *granule cell*) up to about 100 microns for a motor neuron in the spinal cord. Inside of the cell body, many of the specialized proteins and enzymes that participate in the metabolism of the cell are synthesized from the DNA templates contained in the nucleus. The axon exits from the cell body from an elongated portion known as the *axon hillock*.

THE AXON

Leaving the cell body is a long narrow tube, carrying information from the cell body to the ends of the axon where the *terminal boutons* are located. These end terminals are where connections to the dendrites of other nearby neurons are made. The basic message carried by the axon is known as an *action potential* and will be discussed in more detail later. The axon is often surrounded by a myelin sheath, a tube of fatty tissue, actually part of a *glial cell*, and serves to insulate the axon from other axons. As we shall myelin also serves to speed up the conduction of the action potential along the axon. The "white matter" of the brain, making up more than half of the brain volume, is composed mostly of a vast number of these myelinated axons - more than 176,000 km of axons in the brain of a 20 year old male. Some axons are quite short, running only 1-3mm within the brain. Longer axons run up to 170mm within the brain (these are the axons running through the corpus callosum that we discussed earlier) and the longest axons in the human body run all the way from the base of the spine to the toe of the foot through the sciatic nerve, a distance of over one meter. As you have probably guessed, this nerve as well as the others that have been mentioned a number of times so far are really large bundles of axons. For example, the trigeminal nerve, responsible for movement and sensation in the face and head, contains about 150,000 axonal fibers - 140,000 afferent fibers carrying touch, position, pain and temperature information from the skin, muscles, and joints inward to the brain, and another 10,000 efferent fibers that control the muscles of the jaw and throat that allow us to bite, chew and swallow.

NEURON SUBTYPES

There are many different kinds of neurons, each of them adapted to performing a different task within the nervous system. Information from the environment, whether sound, light, taste, or touch, is gathered from the various receptors and sent inwards towards the rest of the nervous system by *sensory neurons*. Sometimes, sensory neurons are specialized for gathering information directly from the environment: for example the cells responsible for sensing pressure on the surface of the skin are a form of sensory neuron. In other cases the cells that are responsible for converting or *transducing* the physical stimuli form the outside world into nerve impulses are not actually sensory neurons but specialized cells known as *receptor cells*: an example of this would be the cells of your inner ear responsible for converting sound vibrations into nervous system activity. In this case the receptor cells connect directly to sensory neurons. At the other end of the chain, *effector neurons*, the most common of which are *motor neurons*, activate the muscles of the body, controlling movement. The motor neurons have their cell bodies within the spinal cord and have long axons that extend out to terminals attached to the individual muscle cells. A nerve impulse or action potential conducted from the motor neuron along its axon will cause the associated muscle to contract. Between the sensory and motor neurons reside the vast majority of the neurons in the nervous system: the *interneurons*. Interneurons come in a number of different varieties, each with different dendrite and axon sizes and shapes. The most common neurons are *multipolar neuron,* comprised of multiple dendrites extending from the cell body and only a single axon. The bipolar neuron has only a single dendrite exiting one side of the cell body with a single axon exiting the other. These neurons are usually sensory neurons whose dendrites terminate at receptor cells. A third type of neuron, the *unipolar neuron*, has only a single process leaving the cell body which eventually branches in two directions, one branch leading to the dendrites and the other along an axon.

Electrical Activity of the Neuron

Before we investigate the operation of the dendrites and axon end terminals, we will describe one of the most basic properties of the neuron: how a neuron's impulse or action potential is initiated and travels from the cell body along the axon to its destination. In order to study how these action potentials occur, we must insert a small recording device known as a *microelectrode* through the cell membrane surrounding the cell into the intracellular fluid contained inside the cell. In this way we can record the electrical potential or voltage across the cell membrane and how this voltage changes across time as the action potential occurs.

THE RESTING POTENTIAL

The first thing we notice when measuring the potential across the membrane is that even when the neuron is at rest there is an electrical potential across the membrane known the resting potential. This causes our measurement equipment to record a constant voltage of -70 mV, meaning that the intracellular fluid of the cell is more negative than the outside of cell, as with a battery. How does this potential come to be? The answer involves the concentration of charged particles known as ions. These ions come in two basic flavours: positive ions or *cations* and negative ions or *anions*, and it is the relative concentrations of positive and negative ions inside and outside of the cell that create the resting potential. Simply put, an excess of positive ions outside of the cell leads to the resting potential. However the real story is more complex than that. There are actually several types of ions involved in generating the resting potential: sodium ions (Na+, with the + sign symbolizing a cation), potassium ions (K+), chloride ions (Cl-, with the − sign symbolizing an anion) and organic anions (symbolized by A-). The organic anions are negatively charged proteins and they exist only on the inside of the cell. The other ion types are found in different concentrations in both the intracellular and extracellular fluid. These concentrations are the result of the balance between two opposing forces: electrostatic pressure and diffusion.

Diffusion

If you were to divide a container of water into two compartments, with only a tiny opening between them, and dissolve an amount of red dye in one chamber, eventually the water in both compartments would have equal concentrations of the dissolved dye and would appear equally red, even without stirring the water. The reason for this is that the heat in the water causes random motion of the dissolved molecules of dye, and the constant bumping and jostling of these molecules causes them to eventually move from areas of high concentration to areas of low concentration. This movement would only cease when the mixture was at a temperature of absolute zero. The force that moves the dissolved molecules from areas of high to low concentration is known as the force of diffusion. As some molecules of dye moved into the second chamber, some molecules of water would move in the other direction, since the water begins in a relatively higher concentration in the other chamber compared to the chamber with the dye.

Electrostatic Pressure

If we were to use a spoonful of table salt in our previous experiment instead of red dye, a different result (with much the same outcome) would occur. Some substances, salt being one of them, when dissolved in water, split into their two ion components. The salt, whose chemical symbol is NaCl or sodium chloride, will split into a positively charged sodium (Na+) ion and a negatively charged chloride ion (Cl-) - some of the very same ions important in establishing the resting potential. Ions with the same charge repel each other - positive ions repel positive ions and negative repel negative - but ions with different charges attract each other. This force of repulsion and attraction is known as electrostatic pressure. In areas with too many positive or negative ions electrostatic pressure will cause the ions to move from these areas to areas with no net charge.

Balance of forces

In our simple salt example, each molecule of NaCl splits into one positive and one negative ion, and since there are equal numbers of positive and negative charges in the compartment, electrostatic pressure does not play much of a role. In this case the force of diffusion would act alone, causing equal numbers of both positive and negative ions to move into the second compartment. However, what if we were to complicate the situation by putting some immobile organic anions (A+) into the first compartment? In this case the negative Cl- cations would be attracted by electrostatic pressure, while the positive Na+ anions would be repelled. This would cause Na+ to move to the other chamber and Cl- to stay. However, this would immediately cause a larger concentration of Na+ in one chamber (and Cl- in the other) and now the force of diffusion would cause the Na+ to move back into the chamber with the A+. Eventually the two forces would balance out, with a few too many charged ions ending up in one or the other of the compartments. The result would be a small voltage potential occurring between the two compartments.

The resting potential in the cell occurs in the same way, with the added complication of the K+ ions. The cell membrane acts as the barrier between the two compartments, and the forces of electrostatic pressure and diffusion balance the relative concentrations of the ions. The organic anions A+ are trapped inside of the cell, being unable to pass through the membrane. The K+ ions are in higher concentration inside of the cell, so the force of diffusion tries to push them out. However, the inside if the cell is more negative than the outside so electrostatic forces attract K+ into the cell. The two forces balance and K+ stays more or less where it is, despite the existence of pores in the cell membrane, known as *leaky potassium channels*. These potassium channels are just like the hole between the two compartments in our simple example, except that they only allow potassium ions, but not sodium or chloride ions, to pass through them. The chloride Cl- ions, unlike K+, are in a higher concentration outside of the cell, and once again the balance of forces provides an explanation. The force of diffusion would push these ions from outside to the inside of the cell where they are in a lower concentration. However, the inside of the cell is more negative, so the force of electrostatic pressure pushes these ions outside of the cell. Once again these two forces balance and the Cl- stays where it is.

Now what about Na+? This is found in a higher concentration outside of the cell. The force of diffusion pushes it into the cell. The inside of the cell is more negative, and unlike charges attract each other, so electrostatic pressure also pulls Na+ into the cell. The two forces in this case are NOT in balance. How does this situation come about? First, the cell membrane is not very permeable to Na+ molecules - there are no convenient leaky Na+ channels to allow movement of Na+ across the membrane. What exists is a special type of molecule embedded in the cell membrane known as a sodium-potassium pump. This pump is an active ion transporter that pushes three Na+ ions outside of the cell and two K+ ions into the cell with each action of the pump. The pump requires energy to operate, which it receives from the inside of the cell in the form of molecules of ATP. Up to 40% of the energy used by the cell is used to power this pump, which is primarily responsible for maintaining the resting potential, keeping more Na+ ions outside of the cell and thus making the inside of the cell 70 mV more negative than the outside.

THE ACTION POTENTIAL

Now that we understand the basic resting state of the neuron, what happens when it is disturbed from its resting state? If we continue to observe the membrane potential of our neuron, sometimes we will see that the potential fluctuates, becoming less negative - we call this reduction in the polarization of the membrane *depolarization*. This represents the action of other neurons communicating with our neuron through its dendrites - we will explain exactly how these communications change the membrane potential later. Since there are many neurons connecting to our neuron, all communicating at different times, sometimes they will cause the membrane potential to move quite far from the resting state. Eventually, the potential will depolarize to a critical point, called the *threshold*, which is usually around -55mV. Now a completely new reaction occurs. The membrane potential starts to change quite rapidly towards 0mV and briefly rises above 0mV until the inside of the cell is actually 40mV more positive than the outside. This brief change begins to subside immediately, taking about 1-2ms to run its course. This change from near threshold, to a positive potential, and then back to the resting state is what is called an *action potential*.

So what changed when the neuron reached its threshold? If we observe the flow of ions across the cell membrane we will have the answer. The cell membrane, which we explained was not very permeable to Na+ ions at the resting potential, suddenly became much more permeable to Na+ - and now both the force of diffusion and electrostatic pressure cause a sudden rush of Na+ inwards, increasing the positive charge inside of the cell. Here another type of ion channel, called a *voltage gated sodium channel*, opens its gate when the membrane potential is below -55mV. When the membrane reaches threshold and the gate opens, Na+ rushes in; these gates close almost immediately, but now the balance of the resting potential has been disturbed and a new sequence of events occurs. We will go through these steps in order:

1. When the membrane reaches threshold, the voltage gated sodium channels open and sodium rushes into the cell. A rapid change in the membrane potential from -55mV to +40mV occurs.

2. Now yet another type of ion channel comes into the picture: *voltage dependent potassium channels*. Unlike the leaky potassium channels that we discussed earlier, which are always open, these channels open when the membrane becomes depolarized. They are slightly less sensitive than the voltage dependent sodium channels, so they will open later. As soon as they begin to open, K+ begins leaving the cell, as the balance of forces keeping it in equilibrium has already been disturbed. Soon we have reached our peak voltage of +40mV, and the sodium channels begin to close, so no more Na+ can enter the cell. The sodium channels become *refractory* - the sodium channel gates close and will not open again for a period of time (the *absolute refractory period*).

3. With the voltage gated K+ channels open, and the inside of the cell more positive than the outside, the K+ ions continue to leave the cell. This outgoing flow of positive charges begins to return the membrane towards the resting potential, and the voltage gated potassium channels begin to close.

4. Once the membrane reaches its resting potential again, the voltage gated K+ channels are fully closed, and K+ stops leaving the cell. At the same time, the voltage-gated sodium channels are reset and the gates are ready to open again in the event that the membrane reaches threshold again. The absolute refractory period is over.

5. Since many K+ ions have recently leaked out of the cell, an accumulation of K+ around the outside of the membrane actually causes the membrane potential to temporarily become *hyperpolarized* - the voltage actually becomes more negative than the resting potential. This period of hyperpolarization lasts 2-3 ms, until the K+ ions in the vicinity of the membrane diffuse away. Although the refractory period is technically over, during this period of hyperpolarization the membrane is relatively difficult to excite and will not likely fire another action potential - this time period is sometimes called the *relative refractory period*. This is important, as we shall see in the next section, in order to keep the action potential moving in one direction along an axon.

There is one further important point about the action potential. Once threshold is reached and the sequence begins, the action potential will occur in exactly the same way each time. There are no larger or smaller action potentials - either an action potential occurs or it does not. This is what is known as the *all-or-none law*. So if every action potential is the same size, how is it that we experience some stimuli as stronger and some weaker? How is it that some muscular contractions are powerful and some are weak? Information about the strength of a stimulus is carried by the *rate* at which a sensory neuron fires - if it only produces occasional action potentials, the stimulus may be weak, whereas if it produces a quick series of action potentials, coming one after the other, the stimulus may be strong. If the motor neuron fires only one or two action potentials, the associated muscle will contract only weakly, while if it fires a burst of action potentials, the muscle will contract strongly.

PROPAGATION OF THE ACTION POTENTIAL ALONG THE AXON

We have so far described the sequence of events that occurs during an action potential for an isolated patch of cell membrane, perhaps at the cell body or in a small stretch along the axon. Now that we understand this, we can begin to study how the neuron transmits information along the axon. Once the cell body is sufficiently depolarized by the action of the dendrites to reach the threshold, the area of membrane at the beginning of the axon where it exits the cell body   Once an action potential is initiated here, this part of the membrane will rapidly depolarize. Electric currents spread out from this depolarized region to neighbouring regions of membrane further down the axon, causing them to reach threshold in turn. The action potential spreads down the axon in this fashion. The hyperpolarization phase that we discussed in the previous section follows the action potential along, preventing it from going backwards again. This spread of the action potential moves at a speed of about 1-2m/s along an unmyelinated axon.

This brings us to the primary purpose of the myelin sheath. Although 1-2m/s is fast enough for a very short axon, it would take more than a second for an action potential to reach your brain from the end of your toe. This is much too long, so almost all of the longer axons in the nervous system are covered in a myelin sheath. This sheath is part of another cell, called an *oligodendrocyte* if the axon is located in the CNS, and a *Schwann cell* in the peripheral nervous system. The axon is covered in discrete segments with patches of bare membrane between segments, called the *nodes of Ranvier*. Since the covered portions of the axon are not in contact with the extracellular fluid, no ion flow occurs - instead the action potential jumps from one node to the next, a process called saltatory conduction. This speeds up the conduction velocity of the action potential by a factor of almost 100.

Communication Between Neurons

As we have seen, each neuron is structured in a way that allows it to receive and transmit information. The operation of a neuron seems fairly simple - it can either fire an action potential or not. In simple organisms such as insects, even a few hundred thousand neurons are able to control complicated operations, such as the flight of a fruit fly. In larger brains, many simple neurons are organized into vast communication networks, and as these networks grow in complexity, the ability of these organized groups of neurons to perform complex calculations grows. A human sized brain, with over 1 million times more neurons than the fruit fly, is able to interpret and solve complex problems, learn from experience, communicate concepts via speech and writing, and perform various other tasks that seem almost miraculous considering the relative simplicity of the individual neuron. The key to how simple individual neurons participate in these complex actions lies in the way that neurons communicate with each other. Neurons communicate via *synaptic transmission* - messages are carried from one neuron to another over a very thin gap between the terminal bouton of one neuron and the dendrite of the next. This gap, called the *synapse* or *synaptic cleft*, is usually about 20 billionths of a meter wide, and is filled with extracellular fluid. When an action potential travels down the axon to its end, the terminal boutons release a *neurotransmitter*, which diffuses across the synaptic cleft and produces a *postsynaptic potential* at the receiving neuron. These postsynaptic potentials are brief depolarizations or hyperpolarizations of the membrane of the receiving neuron that bring it either closer to or further away from its threshold and thus influence the likelihood that an action potential will occur.

THE SYNAPSE

The synapse is the site of communication between two cells, the cell sending the message and the cell receiving it, which we shall often refer to as the pre-synaptic cell and the post-synaptic cell respectively. Since there are two cells, there are of course two sides to the synapse, the pre-synaptic membrane located on the end of the terminal bouton, and the postsynaptic membrane located on the dendrite of the receiving cell, which face each other across the synaptic cleft. Inside of the terminal bouton are a number of *synaptic vesicles*, small rounded bundles covered in the same substance that makes up the cell membrane and containing a small amount of the neurotransmitter chemical. When the action potential arrives from the axon, these vesicles fuse with the pre-synaptic membrane and release the neurotransmitter into the synaptic cleft. From there molecules of the neurotransmitter diffuse across to the postsynaptic membrane where they attach or *bind* themselves to *receptor sites,* proteins that are embedded in the postsynaptic membrane. These postsynaptic receptors are often associated with neurotransmitter-dependent ion channels. When the neurotransmitter binds to the receptor, the gate in this ion channel opens and allows a flow of ions to cross the membrane into the postsynaptic cell producing the postsynaptic potential. If the ion channel is designed to allow a positively polarized ion ($Na+$ for example) to flow into the cell, the postsynaptic potential will be depolarized - an *excitatory post synaptic potential* or *EPSP*. Conversely an ion channel could open that allows $K+$ to flow out of the cell - this would hyperpolarize the membrane, causing an *inhibitory postsynaptic potential* or *IPSP*. EPSPs excite the neuron, making it more likely to produce an action potential, while IPSPs inhibit it, making it less likely to fire.

Once the neurotransmitter has activated the receptors in the postsynaptic membrane, it must be prevented from triggering other unwanted effects at the postsynaptic site. There are two mechanisms in the synapse responsible for this activity. Some neurotransmitters are inactivated by special enzymes that break them down into their constituent chemicals. Other neurotransmitters are re-absorbed into the pre-synaptic cell through a process known as *reuptake.* These two processes terminate the post-synaptic potential.

NEURAL INTEGRATION

We have discussed how neurotransmitter chemicals initiate excitatory and inhibitory post-synaptic potentials, increasing or decreasing the likelihood that a neuron will fire an action potential. Hundreds, even thousands of IPSPs and EPSPs are initiated on a target cell at any given time, and it is the relative balance between excitation and inhibition that determine the rate at which a neuron fires. The IPSPs and EPSPs interact with each other in a process known as *neural*

Draft

integration. We will describe two basic forms of neural integration: *temporal summation* and *spatial summation.* Each EPSP that a neuron receives is quite small, moving the membrane potential only a small amount towards its threshold. However this depolarization lasts for some time, and if the same pre-synaptic neuron causes another EPSP before it fades away, the membrane potential will move yet closer to its threshold. If the pre-synaptic neuron fires a burst of action potentials that is sufficiently rapid and goes on for a long enough time, the neuron receiving these EPSPs will move all the way from its resting state to its threshold, and fire an action potential of its own. This process is known as *temporal summation,* as the activity of many EPSPs at one synapse are summed across time. The other process, *spatial summation,* occurs when several EPSPs from different pre-synaptic neurons occur at exactly the same time. In this situation, the EPSPs summate, moving the membrane potential much closer to threshold than any single EPSP could. If enough EPSPs are received from different neurons at the same time, the neuron will fire an action potential.

What happens when we throw some IPSPs into the mix? The IPSPs are hyperpolarizing, and cause the membrane potential to move away from its threshold. If an EPSP and an IPSP are received from two different pre-synaptic neurons at the same time, they will cancel out, leaving the cells membrane potential more or less at resting state.

NEUROTRANSMITTER AND RECEPTOR TYPES

There are more than a hundred different types of neurotransmitters at work within the nervous system. Each neuron releases only one specific neurotransmitter at all of its terminals, but different neurons release different substances. Each molecule of neurotransmitter has a specific shape, and each receptor molecule is sensitive to only one specific shape of neurotransmitter molecule, allowing only that molecule to bind to its receptor-binding site and activate the associated ion.

Since there are so many neurotransmitter types we only have time to mention a few of them here. *Acetylcholine* is the neurotransmitter released from the motor nerves to the muscle fiber junctions, and was the first neurotransmitter to be identified in 1914. Its joint discoverers Henry Hallett Dale and Otto Loewi were awarded the Nobel Prize for their work. In the CNS, acetylcholine appears to be associated with learning and short-term memory.

Another neurotransmitter is *serotonin,* thought to be involved in the regulation of appetite, emotional arousal, and sleep. Serotonin also appears to have a role in depression, as many individuals with depression appear to have lower concentrations of serotonin in their brain tissue.

Gamma-amino-butyric acid, or *GABA*, is found in most of the inhibitory synapses in the brain. Its excitatory counterpart is *glutamate*, found in most of the fast excitatory synapses.

The final neurotransmitter we will mention here is *dopamine*, which plays a critical role in the reward system of the brain and is involved in many neurological diseases such as Parkinson's disease and schizophrenia.

Glial Cells

We have spent a great deal of time describing the action of neurons, but neurons make up less than half of the cells in the central nervous system. The rest of the cells, *glial cells*, are in some ways the "glue" that holds the nervous system together (glia is the Greek word for glue). We have already mentioned one type of glial cell, the oligodendrocytes, that produce the myelin sheath that surrounds many of the axons in the central nervous system. Another type of glial cell, in fact the most abundant type, is the *astrocyte* or "star cell". These cells send out processes that are wrapped around blood vessels in the brain, or wrapped around parts of the neuron. The astrocyte transfers nutrients from the blood to the neuron when it is needed, and holds the parts of the neuron in place. Other types of astrocytes remove dead neurons from within the brain, and yet others participate in regulating the removal of neurotransmitters from within the synaptic cleft.

The Anatomy of the Nervous System

Terminology

Before we begin describing the various parts of the nervous system, we will need to introduce some terminology. Directions in the nervous system are usually described relative to a line drawn along the spinal cord and through to the front of the brain; this line is referred to as the *neuraxis*. In many animals (i.e., fish) this is a straight line, but in humans this line bends forward as the spine enters the brain. The front of this line is termed *rostral* (towards the head), and the back end is termed *caudal* (towards the tail). The top and back of the head (structures above the neuraxis) are dorsal (think of the dorsal fin on a shark) while the ventral surface faces the ground. Structures closer the centre of the brain are described as more *medial*, while structures farther away from the centre are more *lateral*.

Studying the Brain

The brain is not simply a large mass of undifferentiated tissue. It is not always easy to identify the different structures exist in the brain, and one of the most important challenges has been to determine if different functions of the brain are associated with different structures. One early theory, Franz Joseph Gall's theory of phrenology, pioneered the idea that different brain functions were located in different areas. Unfortunately the details of Gall's proposal were not based on any scientific evidence. He asserted that different mental attributes such as "benevolence" or "hope" or "intelligence" were located in different sub-organs of the brain, and these sub organs would grow with the use of that facility. He believed that the growth of these sub-organs could be measured by looking at the shape of the skull. Unfortunately for his idea, the external shape of the skull has almost nothing to do with the internal conformation of the brain and his theory was eventually discredited. What he did achieve, however, was bringing the attention of more reputable scientists to the idea of the localization of function. Since the days of phrenology, a number of more useful techniques have been developed for studying both the structure and the function of the brain. We will discuss a few of them below.

Lesion Studies

One of the simplest ideas for studying brain function is as follows: if a certain area of the brain is damaged or removed, and a certain function of the brain is lost (such as memory, or vision), that structure can be associated with that brain function. Although it is of course unethical to deliberately damage the brain of a human, such experiments can be done on animals. Such experiments began as early as 1825 by Pierre Florens, who developed techniques for surgically removing or *ablating* parts of the brains of pigeons and studying the results. For example, he discovered that removal of a part of the brain called the cerebellum affected the birds' motor coordination, and removal of another structure called the medulla interfered with vital functions such as heartbeat and respiration. Studies that remove parts of animal's brains in order to study the result are known as *ablation studies*. In humans, the approach taken (which still continues to this day) is to examine patients with accidental brain damage to determine both the site of the brain damage (often done during autopsy after the patient's death) and the nature of the functional changes in their behaviour. One of the most famous cases of this type was the case of Phineas Gage. Phineas was a railroad construction foreman who in 1848 survived an accident where a large iron rod was driven completely through his head, destroying a large part of his left frontal lobe. After a long and difficult convalescence, Gage eventually recovered, but his personality was greatly changed. Before the accident he was a capable and efficient foreman, while afterwards he was described as "fitful, irreverent, and grossly profane, showing little deference for his fellows". He appeared to be unable to plan his future actions and was constantly changing from one idea to the next. This suggested that the frontal lobes were responsible for functions like planning and impulse-control, and later studies have confirmed these ideas.

Electrical Stimulation and Single Cell recording

Rather than removing a part of the brain and trying to determine what function is lost, we could take a different approach - stimulating a part of the brain and trying to determine what brain function is elicited. This was the approach taken by neurosurgeon Wilder Penfield in a famous series of experiments that he published in 1951. Penfield had performed brain surgery on epileptic patients in order to surgically remove the focus of the epileptic activity from the brain, and although removing any brain tissue could potentially lead to some later impairment, he was anxious to avoid cutting into what we now call the *eloquent* areas of the brain, or the *eloquent cortex*. The eloquent cortex consists of those areas where damage would lead to paralysis, loss of language ability, or loss of sensory processing. At the time these areas were not fully mapped out, so Penfield took the opportunity of having a partially exposed brain to do some experiments and help his patients at the same time. Since the patients were under local anaesthesia, Penfield could use an electrical probe to stimulate various parts of the brain, while at the same time asking the patients what they were feeling. In this way he mapped out the sensory and motor areas of the brain (you will see a diagram of the cortical homunculus that he developed in a later section). He was also able to identify other areas i.e., where stimulation led to the vivid recall of past memories. Although the general features of these brain maps are very similar across patients, the exact details can vary quite considerably from person to person, and this type of mapping is usually still performed on each patient during brain surgery. These maps are also supplemented by a battery of other functional brain studies (some of which we will discuss in a moment) performed prior to surgery.

In animal studies, we can get even more detailed information about the operation of the living brain by recording brain activity with microelectrodes. In fact, much of the information you have already learned about action potentials and membrane dynamics was obtained by inserting microelectrodes into the axon of giant squid, stimulating the axon, and recording activity. In squids and other marine animals, the diameter of the axon is quite large - up to 1mm; this is an adaptation that speeds up the transmission of the action potential since neurons in these animals lack myelin. Physiologists Alan Hodgkin and Andrew Huxley performed experiments that uncovered most of what we know about how ions flow during the action potential using microelectrodes inserted into these squid axons. For this work, published in 1952, they won the Nobel Prize. Because their electrodes were relatively crude, the giant axon was a necessity- today, however, we have available microelectrodes with tip diameters of less than micrometer that can be inserted through the cell membrane of a single cell of a living animal without causing undue damage, in order to obtain *intracellular recordings*. The responses recorded by these electrodes are known as *single-unit recordings*. Groups of larger electrodes may also be inserted into the brain tissue of an awake, behaving animal in order to obtain *extracellular recordings*. The recorded responses from the array of electrodes is then processed by computer in order to separate the individual action potentials from any cell bodies that are near the electrode tips - activity from several cells cab be simultaneously recorded with this technique. Using these techniques to record the activity of single cells in rats led to the discovery of *place cells* in a part of the brain known as the hippocampus. By letting the rats wander around in their environment while recording the activity of individual cells, it was discovered that some cells would fire only when the rat was in a certain area of the cage, say near the door, while another cell might fire when the rat was near the food dish. It was hypothesized from this that a cognitive map of the environment is located in the hippocampus of the rat.

Structural Neuroimaging

As has been described, clinical lesion studies often rely on an autopsy of the patient to determine the nature of the brain damage. This approach has a number of drawbacks - for example, after an extensive behavioural study of an interesting patient, he might live for many years, or the relatives may decline to give permission for an autopsy when he dies. For this reason, neuroscientists make use of a number of techniques for studying the structure of the living human brain, doing so *noninvasively* - that is without any surgery to open the skull.

X-RAY CT

The first method developed for imaging the brain was computerized x-ray tomography or CT for short. In this technique, the patient's head is placed in a ring containing an x-ray emitter and detector on opposite sides of the patient's head. The ring rotates while the emitter passes x-rays through the patient's head to the detector. The detector's response is recorded from all angles through the patient's head, and a computer is used to reconstruct an image of the brain. This technique is able to distinguish different tissue types to some extent, and will be able to show areas of damage due to stroke if the image is taken early enough. The CT will not, however, show tumours unless they are large enough to distort the underlying structure of the brain, since tumour tissue and normal brain tissue absorb about the same amount of x-rays. CT scans, however, subject individuals to a moderate to high dosage of radiation and thus pose a level of cancer risk.

MRI

The MRI, like the CT, involves placing the head of individuals inside a large ring. The MRI, however, uses a very strong magnetic field to image the brain, a process known *magnetic resonance imaging*. When tissue is placed inside of a strong magnetic field and is excited by a radio frequency pulse, the molecules in the body will vibrate at a certain rate, emitting their own radio frequency waves. An antenna called a *head coil* picks up these radio waves and records them for computer analysis. Different molecules will produce slightly different radio waves, and the computer will decode this information, producing exquisitely detailed pictures of different slices of the brain. The MRI is able to determine the difference between different tissue types, for example grey and white matter.

Functional Neuroimaging

Although the CT scan and the MRI can provide us with the ability to noninvasively describe the structure of the brain, the techniques for studying the actual function of the brain that we have discussed so far, like ablation studies or electrical stimulation of the brain surface, are far from non-invasive. There are, however, some techniques that allow us to learn things about brain function noninvasively.

POSITRON EMISSION TOMOGRAPHY

Whenever a neuron fires an action potential, a certain amount of energy is required, for things like pumping the excess Na+ back out of the cell, for creating new vesicles of neurotransmitter to replace those used, for removing the excess neurotransmitter from the synaptic cleft, and so on. When a particular area of the brain is particularly active, the corresponding neurons fire action potentials at an elevated rate, and thus this area will require a great deal more energy than less active areas. One of the main sources of energy for a cell is glucose, carried into the area via the bloodstream. If we could measure the amount of glucose consumed by a particular area of the brain, we would know how active it is. This is the basis of *positron emission tomography scanning*, or *PET* scanning. In order to find where the glucose is being consumed, a person in a PET scan is injected with a mildly radioactive form of glucose. This substance, known as a *radionuclide*, is an isotope with a very short half-life, meaning that half the radioactive particles will decay back into a non-radioactive form in a very short time, typically in less than an hour. Each time a radioactive particle decays, it emits 2 positrons that shoot out in opposite directions. A ring of detectors around the individual's head detects the positrons and a computer calculates the exact location of the positron emission. In this way the amount of glucose being used by each brain area can be calculated, giving us an image of the amount of brain activity in a particular area. This image is typically overlaid on a picture of the individual's brain anatomy recorded from an MRI scan. There are several disadvantages to this technique though. First, the production of radionuclides is very expensive, requiring an atomic particle accelerator, and since the half-life is so short they must be used almost immediately. Second, the radionuclide must be injected into an artery, which although relatively safe is not completely non-invasive. Third, the person being scanned is exposed to a small dose of radiation (about 3-4 times that of a CT scan), posing a minimal cancer risk.

Of course one of the problems with this technique is that ALL areas of the brain are at least a little bit active all of the time, and would all emit some radioactive particles. Furthermore, if we were trying, for example, to find out what brain areas were active while a subject listened to music, the subject would still likely have his eyes open and stimulation of the visual areas of his brain would also occur. For such reasons, the PET scan can only provide limited specific functional localization information.

THE FUNCTIONAL MRI OR FMRI

We have already said that the MRI gives structural but not functional information about the brain. This technique can be modified slightly so that it may provide similar functional data as the PET scan. Another requirement of a highly active neuron is oxygen, carried into the area via the blood supply from the lungs. When an area of the brain is activated, the capillaries supplying blood to the area will dilate and the blood supply to the area will increase (after about 3-5 seconds). The oxygen molecules attached to the haemoglobin in the blood are then used up. This leads to slight changes in the magnetic properties of the blood, and these responses are recorded by the MRI. Rapidly scanning an area of the brain and searching for changes in the magnetic properties of the blood can measure the amount of activity in a particular area of the brain. Very detailed images of brain activation with a resolution of 1mm can thus be produced in a completely non-invasive fashion, without the requirement of expensive radionuclides. There are, however, still some disadvantages to this technique. Since the blood oxygen response takes some seconds to build up, very short brain events are difficult to measure. fMRI also is only an indirect measure of neural activity and thus measurements provided may be influenced by non-neural activity, and like the PET scan can only provide limited specific functional localization information.

THE ELECTROENCEPHALOGRAM OR EEG

When a neuron fires an action potential, it produces a small amount of electrical current that can be measured from outside of the cell. If enough neurons fire at the same time, this electrical activity can easily be detected outside of the brain at the surface of the scalp. An electroencephalogram is the record of this electrical activity collected from an array of electrodes attached to an individual's scalp. These recordings are used to diagnose epilepsy as well as various brain injuries. The different stages of sleep all have different EEG signatures, and the EEG can also detect how attentive or relaxed an individual is. The EEG does suffer the same limitation as the other techniques though, in that all of the brain is active all of the time. This makes it difficult to distinguish the brain activity caused by a particular event as it is drowned out by all the background activity. The technique of recording the *event-related potential* or *ERP* can be used to overcome this limitation. By recording the EEG response to a stimulus over tens or hundreds of trials and averaging the EEG responses to all of these events, the background activity becomes greatly attenuated and the electrical activity evoked by the stimulus is revealed. By using up to 256 electrodes positioned all over the scalp, the approximate location of the evoked activity can be inferred. Although the resolution of this localization is not as precise as the fMRI, the EEG is able to measure very short brain responses as it takes a sample of brain activity thousands of times per second.

Brain Anatomy

The Ventricles and the Cerebrospinal Fluid

The brain is a fairly delicate structure, and evolution has taken certain steps to protect it from injury. The brain actually floats in a liquid bath of *cerebrospinal fluid* or *CSF*, and is only loosely attached to the skull by a network of filaments called *arachnoid trabeculae.* The CSF extends down into the spinal cord, and up into the centre of the brain through a system of interconnected chambers known as *ventricles.* About 500 ml of fresh CSF is secreted into the ventricles each day by special cells in its lining and flows through the network to be re-absorbed by other cells in the area between the brain and the skull. Besides providing protection from injury by suspending the brain, CSF also serves to rinse metabolic waste out of the central nervous system.

The Hindbrain

The hindbrain surrounds the fourth ventricle and consists of two major divisions: the myelencephelon, consisting of one major structure, the *medulla* or *medulla oblongata,* and the metencephalon.

The metencephalon is further subdivided into the *cerebellum* and the *pons.* The medulla, the pons, and the midbrain (discussed in the next section), are collectively referred to as the *brainstem.*

THE CEREBELLUM

Cerebellum is Latin for "little brain" – an appropriate name considering the cerebellum resembles a miniature version of the rest of the brain, with two hemispheres and a deeply folded surface. The cerebellum receives information from almost all of the senses: visual, auditory, vestibular (the position of the head), and somatosensory (the sense of touch and the positions of the various joints). The cerebellum also receives information about all of the individual muscle movements controlled by the motor areas of the brain, and its function is to produce corrections to these movements by taking into account the information from the senses. If the cerebellum is damaged, almost all motor activity is impaired – walking and even standing become difficult, and any other coordinated muscle movement becomes jerky and inaccurate.

THE PONS

The pons appears as a bulge on the ventral surface near the top of the brainstem, rostral to the medulla and inferior to the midbrain. The core of the pons is part of the reticular formation (discussed below). The pons also contains groups of relay nuclei that pass signals to the cerebellum from higher brain centers, and nuclei involved in sleep, respiration, and eye movement.

THE MEDULLA

The medulla forms one of the centers involved in the control of the autonomic nervous system. The medulla controls respiration, taking signals about the amount of oxygen in the blood from special receptors in the carotid artery and using these signals to control the respiratory rate. It also regulates the heart rate, and contains centers that control reflexes such as swallowing, sneezing, and vomiting.

THE RETICULAR FORMATION

Ascending through the middle of the medulla and the pons, and further up through the brainstem to the thalamus is an area of the brain stem known as the reticular formation. The reticular formation functions to control the general arousal of the brain, particularly the cerebral hemispheres. As such it appears to be intimately involved in controlling such processes as sleep and wakefulness, sexual arousal, and the ability to concentrate. Damage to the reticular formation can cause an individual to lose consciousness and become completely comatose.

The Midbrain

The midbrain, or mesencephelon, located rostral to the pons along the neuraxis, consists of two major structures, the tectum and the tegmentum. A chamber filled with CSF, the cerebral aqueduct, runs through the centre of the midbrain, joining the third and fourth ventricles.

The tectum is located on the dorsal side of the midbrain, and contains centers for both auditory and visual processing. The visual area is known as the superior colliculus; it controls eye movements, and is responsible for some visual reflexes and reactions to moving stimuli. The tegmentum, on the ventral side, contains some of the nuclei of the reticular formation that we have already mentioned, as well as two other important nuclei: the red nucleus and the substantia nigra. Both of these are important components of the motor system. The *substantia nigra* (latin for "black substance") appears darker than the surrounding tissue because some of the neurons contain high levels of melanin. Degeneration of neurons in this area lead to the symptoms of Parkinson's disease, that is, motor problems such as tremors and rigidity. The neurons in this area secrete the neurotransmitter dopamine, which plays an important role in the reward system of the brain and is implicated in addiction. The *red nucleus* has partial control over gait, controlling arm swinging during walking and the crawling of babies.

The Forebrain

The forebrain consists of two major divisions: the telencephalon, consisting of the cerebral cortex and a few other structures, and the diencephalon, situated between the telencephalon and the midbrain. The telencephalon is of such importance that it rates its own section. In this section we will discuss the important structures of the diencephalon, which are located near the middle of the brain, with the cerebral cortex wrapped around them.

HYPOTHALAMUS

The hypothalamus is located just above the brainstem, under the thalamus. It controls and organizes behaviours of the autonomic nervous system related to survival of the organism, the so-called four F's: fighting, feeding, fleeing and mating. Although it is relatively small, the hypothalamus is actually an extremely complex area with a number of nuclei involved in multiple functions. The hypothalamus has been shown to be involved in such diverse activities as urinary control, thirst and hunger, and even shivering. One of its most important functions is to secrete hormones that control the activity of the pituitary gland and thus forms the main link between the nervous system and the endocrine system.

PITUITARY GLAND

A special system of blood vessels known as the pituitary stalk connects the hypothalamus to a tiny endocrine gland about 5mm in diameter that protrudes from the base of the hypothalamus. Cells in the hypothalamus secrete hormones that in turn stimulate the pituitary gland to release its own hormones. Many of these hormones, in turn, lead yet other glands in the endocrine system to release their hormones, and it has therefore been referred to as the "master gland". The hormones secreted by the posterior pituitary gland are produced in the hypothalamus, and include oxytocin, which acts as a neurotransmitter in the brain and has a variety of influences on such behaviours as breastfeeding and other maternal behaviours, as well as sexual orgasm. The posterior pituitary also releases the hormone vasopressin, which regulates water, glucose, and salt in the blood. The anterior pituitary synthesizes a number of hormones under control of the hormones released from the hypothalamus, such as thyroid -stimulating hormone, which in turn causes the thyroid to produce the hormone thyroxin, which controls the rate of many metabolic processes in the body.

Draft

THALAMUS

The thalamus is located on the dorsal portion of the diencephalon, near the middle of the cerebral hemispheres. It is a symmetrical structure, having a left and right lobe with identical sets of nuclei. The thalamus acts as a relay station between all of the sensory systems (except olfaction) and the cerebral cortex. As well as relaying the sensory information to the cortex, it also does some preliminary processing of the information.

AMYGDALA

The amygdala, together with the hippocampus, are often grouped together under the term 'limbic system'. The amygdala might be better referred to as the amagdalae (the plural), since there are two of these structures located within the temporal lobe of each hemisphere of the cerebral cortex. The amygdala is involved in learning, especially in storing memories about emotional events. It is also used to help recognize the emotions of other individuals.

HIPPOCAMPUS

The hippocampus is also a paired structure, with one half located in each cortex. As we have already noted in our discussion of place cells, the hippocampus appears to be the location of where our awareness of our location in space is processed, but it also plays an important role in the formation of other memories, specifically our *declarative memory system* (memories for facts and events that can be explicitly verbalized). Damage to the hippocampus results in severe memory deficits, and our study of these deficits has helped our understanding of exactly how memories are stored in the brain. We will discuss these findings in more detail in a later section.

The Cerebral Cortex

The cerebral cortex is a convoluted structure surrounding the two cerebral hemispheres, containing the limbic system, and another set of sub-cortical structures known as the basal ganglia. The grooves in the cortical surface are known as the sulci - particularly large grooves are referred to as fissures. The two halves of the cortex are separated by the medial longitudinal fissure. The ridges between the sulci are known as gyri, and together they serve to greatly enlarge the surface area of the cortex without increasing its volume. Only about 1/3 of the surface is even visible from outside the brain, the rest is buried deep within the sulci. If unfolded, in humans, the cerebral cortices would have a total surface area of approximately 2500 cm^2. In comparison, the dolphin has a cortical area of 3745 cm^2 and the African elephant, 6300 cm^2 - so the human can hardly lay claim to being the animal with the largest brain. The cortex is only about 3mm thick but it is differentiated into six layers. Neurons in the different layers connect to each other to form small neural circuits capable of simple calculations. Although the cortex is split into two hemispheres, these two hemispheres are not identical - there are actually about 200 million more neurons on the left side than the right. We will discuss some other differences between the two cortices later. In evolutionary terms, this is the newest part of the brain, and is responsible for most key functions that distinguish humans from less advanced animals: awareness, consciousness, thought, planning, and language, to name a few.

Anatomists divided each hemisphere into four main lobes, each named for the nearest cranial bone: the frontal, parietal, occipital, and temporal lobes. The frontal lobe includes everything forward of the *central sulcus*. On the other side of the central sulcus, caudal to the frontal lobe, is the parietal lobe. The temporal lobe joins the bottom of the parietal lobe and extends forward below the frontal lobe. The occipital lobe is located at most caudal part of the brain.

Different areas of the cortex are associated with different functions. The *primary sensory projection areas* are the areas where information from the senses is first received. Visual information is first received in the *primary visual cortex,* located at the very back of the occipital cortex in and around the calcarine fissure. Auditory information is received by primary auditory cortex, located on the medial surface of the temporal lobe. Primary somatosensory cortex is located in the parietal cortex, on the surface directly adjacent to the central sulcus. All three of these areas contain a map of the sensory surface - this is best understood by a look at the somatosensory cortex. The *sensory homunculus* provides a visual representation of how a map of the surface of the skin is represented on the cortical surface. Certain areas seem grossly distorted, for example the surface of the fingers, because they are very sensitive to touch information and therefore have more cortical area dedicated to processing their signals. The primary motor cortex, located directly across the central sulcus from the primary somatosensory cortex, is the last cortical area from which commands are sent to the muscles. It too contains a form of map of the muscles of the body, since different spots on this cortical area are responsible for controlling specific muscles. A *motor homunculus*, analogous to the sensory homunculus, provides a representation of this organization.

Only about 25% of the cortex is dedicated to primary areas. Areas outside of the primary projection areas are often termed *association cortex.* These areas perform increasingly complex functions on the information from the nearby projection areas. For example, areas near primary auditory cortex are responsible for decoding sounds into words, and areas near primary visual cortex are responsible for recognizing objects. As we move further away from the primary areas, these functions become increasingly abstract. Areas in the frontal lobes near primary motor area are responsible for planning and organizing complex motor movements, but areas further forward are involved in planning in general, helping us choose right from wrong and evaluating the consequences of future actions.

Chapter

4

Sensory Systems

You will recall from earlier chapters our discussion of the role of Empiricism in the development of modern science, and the resulting emphasis on objectivity. If we are to consider only objective evidence when testing some hypothesis, how do we decide if the evidence is objective or not? In general, we have relied on the kinds of things that can be independently observed or experienced. For example, we may not be able to observe and agree upon the emotional state that exists inside another person's head, but we can observe and agree on their behaviour, which we assume was produced by these internal emotional events. One immediate consequence of this reliance on objectively observable data is that we rely primarily on our sensory abilities, rather than our rational or logical abilities, to evaluate the outcomes of our investigations. In science, the variables we manipulate and measure must be things we can see (or hear, smell, feel, etc...) in order for us to be able to agree on the results.

This raises some very important questions, which have profound implications for the conduct of science: Do our senses actually give us an accurate picture of the world around us? To what extent can we rely on them to tell us what is really going on 'out there'? In order to answer these questions, we first need to understand how these processes work, and how information about the world gets from 'out there' to 'in here'.

From the psychological perspective there are actually two different things going on when we interact with the environment. Sensory systems are used to gather information, and then this information must be interpreted. For example, what happens when we see something? First, there is the process of *sensation*. While you may be familiar with this word, in the present context we are referring to those processes involved in transforming the physical characteristics of the world into electrical signals in our nervous systems. In the case of vision, this would involve photons (i.e., light 'particles') hitting the retina of the eye, and beginning a series of events in visual receptor cells that result in an electrical signal being transmitted down the optic nerve, a process known as *transduction*. Whatever information is carried in those photons has now made the transition from 'out there' to 'in here'. This, however, is where the process of <u>sensation</u> stops, more or less. Note that at this point, you are not consciously aware of seeing anything yet. In order for you to actually be 'aware' of whatever it is that you are seeing, much more processing needs to take place. All this processing is referred to as *perception*, and while sensory processes may seem somewhat complex, they are probably far simpler and better understood than the processing that subsequently takes place. In terms of vision, that initial signal traveling along the optic nerve (which, as you will see, has some interesting architecture itself) will first reach the *lateral geniculate nucleus* (LGN), a part of the thalamus located in the midbrain in each hemisphere. The information is separated into (simply speaking) colour information and movement information at this level, and each is processed separately. It is not until the next stage, when the signals pass from the LGN to the primary visual cortex (right under your skull, where it sticks out farthest at the back of your head) that the process of actually figuring out what it is that you are looking at begins. This process involves several more layers of processing, as small features are identified and built up into a bigger, identifiable image. Simply becoming aware of seeing something, however, is not the end of the story. This information will pass from the primary visual cortex to a variety of other brain areas. Now that you know <u>what it is</u>, your brain can start working on <u>what it means</u>.

The above is an extremely simplified version of an extremely complex, and not completely understood, story. Many of the sensory and perceptual processes involved in vision and audition will be discussed in quite some detail in the coming lectures. We will now turn to a couple of general issues that inform the study of sensation and perception.

How Accurate are our Sensations and Perceptions?

How accurate is our perception of the world around us? Not nearly as accurate as you might think. For one thing, our sensory organs have physical limitations. Our visual systems respond to a narrow segment of the electromagnetic spectrum, and any wavelengths that are too long (e.g., ultraviolet light) or too short (e.g., infrared light) don't have any effect, and we don't see them. That doesn't mean they are not there. In fact, many other species can see these wavelengths. There is a common 'mind-bender' that is often brought out in the presence of various social lubricants that asks "if there was another colour, what would it look like?" If you were a pigeon, you would have an answer for this question. Pigeons, like many birds, have a more sensitive and complex system of colour vision than humans (for pigeons, there seem to be five primary colours, not three), and they can see infrared light. The same kind of thing can be said about your hearing: You only hear things within a certain range of frequencies. Below this range, you might feel vibration, but you won't really 'hear' anything. Above this range, your auditory apparatus won't respond at all. Nevertheless, dogs, bats, rats, and animals of all kinds can hear sounds that are above our upper frequency limit. Whales and other marine animals may be able to hear frequencies below our lower limit, as well. The point of all this is that, of the entire 'world' that is out there, we are physically capable of being aware of only a small slice of it.

Nor does the problem stop here. Of all the information gathered by our sensory organs, only a small fraction of this actually makes it to the level of our conscious awareness. At each stage of processing, much of this information will be filtered out. (Incidentally, this a good thing. Your mind would be completely overwhelmed very quickly if you attended to all the available incoming information from your sensory systems. The topic of Attention will be explored in greater detail in Term 2). For example, assuming that you are reading this in a sitting position, you were probably not aware until about 2 seconds from now of the pressure of the chair on your body. Now you are aware of it, because you were just made to think about it. However, that sensory input does not 'go away' just because you stop paying attention to it. Most of the time, some part of your brain makes the call that the continuous and unchanging 'body pressure' is not a priority that needs to be dealt with, and this sensory information never gets fully processed. Huge amounts of sensory input, particularly if that input doesn't change over time, is routinely ignored and/or discarded by the brain, and similar things are happening all the time in all of our sensory modalities.

The Inventing Brain

Further complicating the picture, one of the things our brains are best at is 'making things up'. You are all familiar with the brain's ability to fantasize and imagine, but many students are surprised to learn how much of what they perceive of the world around them is invented by the brain, and not actually taken directly from the world itself. One commonly cited example of the brain making up stories at a pretty low perceptual level is the fact that (assuming you have normal vision) you are not aware that you actually have a large blind spot in the visual field of each eye. As you will learn, the physiology of the eye guarantees that it is impossible to see anything in this part of the visual field, yet we are not aware of these blind spots. At some level of processing, our brains take a look at the visual input from the area around the blind spot and decide what ought to be there. This information gets 'pasted in' to our visual input seamlessly, and at no time (except for certain specifically contrived situations, like the one in your text) can we tell the difference between the information we obtained from the real world and the information our brain invented and added to the picture.

Another, often entertaining, means of demonstrating that your brain 'invents' a lot of what you perceive are a class of phenomena called illusions. We will explore several informative examples in the lectures. Below, you will see one of the simplest visual illusions (at least, one of the easiest to draw), the Muller-Lyer illusion.

In this case, it is easy to determine (all you need is a ruler) that our brains are altering the sensory input in some way. Even knowing that this is an illusion does not prevent you from 'seeing' that the straight line segment in B is longer than in A, when in fact they are exactly the same length. In other cases, we can catch the brain repeatedly changing the story it tells us, when the 'world' isn't changing at all. Stare at the figure below for a while and try to decide which surface is the 'front' of the cube.

You will probably notice that which surface appears to be closest to us, the upper right square or the lower left square, will change every few seconds. The interesting thing here is not that the brain has trouble deciding; the image is purposely constructed to be ambiguous in this regard. The interesting thing is that the whole problem arises because the brain is trying to tell us a three-dimensional story based on entirely two-dimensional evidence. Your brain is making you see depth in the image, when there is no actual depth. The image is, in reality, a completely flat figure. The illusion arises when the brain inserts some depth information into the image. As with the blind spot example, the brain is going to try to construct a story that 'makes sense' based on the available input. Unfortunately, in this case there are two equally good 3-D stories that could be told, and no good way for the brain to choose between them. Further, the brain does not simply give up and say "I can't decide", it flips back and forth, first telling us one story is true, then telling us the other story is true. You can stare at the above image for hours, and it will continue to 'flip' every few seconds (don't take that as a suggestion, unless you have a lot of free time).

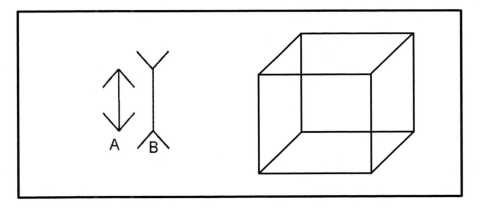

The process of perception almost always involves making 'choices', at some level, among various possible interpretations of sensory input. The example above involves a situation where two equally good interpretations are available. In many other cases, these kinds of decisions are made much more quickly and predictably, because the brain typically prefers certain types of interpretations. One case in which this can happen is when the brain receives conflicting information from two sensory systems. This does not necessarily mean that the 'preferred' explanations are correct. For example, consider ventriloquism: The performance of a ventriloquist involves presenting you with 'information' in two different modalities. First, there are the visual aspects, typically a human being holding some sort of puppet with moving mouth parts. Second, there are the auditory aspects, typically the human half of the act carrying on a conversation with himself. As you probably know, the hard part of being a ventriloquist is being able to produce recognizable speech while not moving your lips, but many people seem to have mastered this particular trick. However, even the best ventriloquist can't defy the laws of physics. When we witness the performance, the auditory information we receive (the 'two voices') is all really coming from the same source (the human). As you will hear in lectures, our ability to *localize* sounds (i.e., to identify the direction and distance of the sound source) is actually pretty good. This ability to localize sounds is good enough, in fact, that when our brains are processing the auditory part of the ventriloquist act, at this level the brain 'knows' the sound is all coming from one place, and not two different places.

The visual information, on the other hand, presents a different picture. What we <u>see</u> when we watch the ventriloquist is the human mouth moving, and then the puppet mouth moving, and this is pretty similar to what we have seen countless times when two individuals have a conversation. Based on what we see, we would <u>expect</u> the sounds of the 'two voices' to be coming from different locations. This visual interpretation of the scene actually 'trumps' the auditory interpretation, and we actually hear the puppet's 'voice' coming from the puppet. Note that the conflict doesn't just result in one kind of sensory information being ignored, one of the streams of information is actually <u>altered</u> to 'fit' with the other. A similar phenomenon occurs when you are watching my talking head shots in the web lectures. Although you understand that the sound of my voice is originating from the speakers beside your computer, it's natural for you to look at my image and think of the speech sounds originating from the video image of my mouth. Assuming you have a good connection, the movements of my mouth correspond with the sounds that reach your ears. If you have a slower connection and my mouth movements fall out of synch with the audio, the illusion is eliminated.

The illusion of ventriloquists and web lecturers alike, is an example of *visual capture*. This refers to the fact that when humans are presented with conflicting information from two different sensory systems, and one of those systems is the visual system, we are strongly predisposed to interpret the visual version of events as the correct one. This is a reflection of the relative importance of vision to humans, compared to the other senses. We rely primarily on vision to identify food, danger, and possibly most importantly, each other. While this particular sensory orientation is not unique to humans (e.g., many species of bird are also highly reliant on vision), it is certainly not universal. Rats, for example, are much more likely to rely on what they smell or hear than on what they see in interpreting the world around them. If a rat's eyes and nose were telling different stories, the rat would almost certainly behave as if the 'nose' version of events was the correct one (i.e., *olfactory* capture).

Finally, you should note that, despite all the examples above, our sensory and perceptual abilities usually work pretty well. After all, these systems evolved along with the rest of the organism, and must have provided some adaptive advantage. If these systems consistently mislead us about the nature of reality, it is hard to imagine how we could be successful as a species. Illusions, and other situations where our sensory/perceptual apparatus seems to fail us in this regard, are often either relatively rare occurrences in nature, or carefully constructed artificial situations designed to exploit some 'loophole' in the system. In fact, finding situations in which these processes come to the wrong conclusions is often one of the most useful ways of figuring out how they work in general. We will now turn to the science of actually measuring the sensitivity of our sensory and perceptual apparatus.

Introduction to Vision

It's often tempting to compare the eyes to a camera. Like a camera, the eyes allow light to enter through a small frontal opening. Our eyes use an auto-focusing, adjustable lens to project light onto the back of the eyeball, and our retina acts like film. But that's where the similarities end. The instant that light hits the retina, our visual system begins to interpret the information provided. Details about shapes, edges, and brightness are processed in a way that our brain can use to make sense of the world. For instance, take a look at the Müller-Lyer illusion (Figure #.1). Can you see which line is longer? The answer is that both lines are exactly the same width, but we don't perceive this to be the case! Visual illusions like this are fascinating to vision scientists because they highlight a unique aspect about how our visual system works to interpret the world.

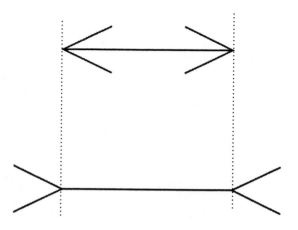

Figure 1. Although both lines are equal in length, our visual system perceives the lines as larger or smaller based on the direction of the arrows. This optical illusion gives us some insight to how our visual system interprets the environment.

Figure 1.

The eye is a truly amazing sensory organ because it plays such an important role in how we interact with the environment. Vision is our primary sensory modality and our eyes are responsible for experiencing colours, shapes, motion and detail. We use our eyes to define resources, potential mates, and dangers, to explore and even to learn. Moreover, neuroscientists think of the eyes as window to the brain, as if they eyes are actually a part of the central nervous system. The eyes are often used as diagnostic tool, to check the health of a person's nervous system, such as a stroke or neurological damage

Vision and the visual system is the most studied sensory modality. There a few important reasons why this is so. First, The sheer magnitude of processing power devoted to vision is staggering: 30% of our brain is devoted to processing vision, taking up more processing power than any other neural function. Second, scientist are very interested in understanding how the brain learn, develops, and forms connections based on sensory experience. Vision provides an excellent tool to do this because it is much easier to manipulate stimuli that we can use to test visual function than any other sensory modality. Using vision, we have been able to understand very broad reaching principles about plasticity in the brain, how the brain forms neural circuits and how nature (genetics) and nurture (sensory experience) shapes the development of those connections.

Draft

The Stimulus

Physical Characteristics of Light

What we perceive as 'light' is an electromagnetic radiation that stimulates the photoreceptors in the back of our eyes. Our eyes are only sensitive to a limited range of the electromagnetic spectrum, called the visible portion of the electromagnetic spectrum. This visible region consists of a spectrum of wavelengths from approximately 360nm to 750nm. Not only can we perceive this radiation, we are also very sensitive to changes of electromagnetic waves within this range.

Light can be described in terms of both particles (the quantum theory of light) and waves. In understanding how the eye works, we will find both theories useful depending on the neurophysiological and psychological behaviour we are describing. By understanding light as a wave, we can understand and describe many of the perceptual properties of light. For example, understanding light as a wavelength is useful when talking about colour.

Isaac Newton first described the wave nature of light, and demonstrated that if he passed light through a prism it would separate into specific ordered, coloured components; red, orange, yellow, green, blue, indigo, and violet, or ROY G BIV for short (Figure #.2). He also showed that these colours are elementary components of the colour spectrum; that is, they cannot be further divided.

Our perception of colour is not limited to the 7 basic elements of colour., within this spectrum we perceive 3 independent sensibilities: hue (wavelength), saturation, and brightness (amplitude).

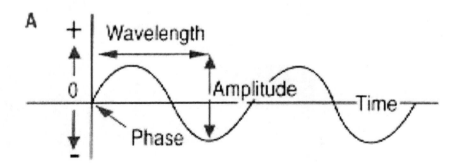

(Figure 2)

Hue refers to what most people mean when they name a colour. It is the psychological dimension that corresponds most closely to the wavelength of light. Our eyes are sensitive to wavelengths of light from 360 to 750 nm. The perception of colour in this visible spectrum changes gradually from blue at the short wavelengths, through green, to red at the long wavelengths. We only have a few names for hues, but experiments have shown that we are capable of discriminating over 200 different hues.

Saturation describes the purity of a hue (Figure 3). A completely saturated colour is the truest version of that colour. Mixing two pure lights (such as laser beams) together will produce a less saturated, intermediate hue. If a light is very impure, containing lots of wavelengths, it will look grey. There are 20 distinguishable steps of saturation for each hue.

Brightness reflects the sum of the responses of all photoreceptors (Figure 3). As the amplitude of the waveform increases, the more energy it contains, and the light is perceived as brighter. We are sensitive to over 500 steps of brightness.

There seems to be a lot of information in the electromagnetic spectrum that we can use in our perception of colour. If we consider all possible combinations of Hues, brightness and saturation (200x20x500), our visual system is capable of distinguishing around two million colour variations!

Figure 3: Saturation and Brightness. (Top) Saturation refers to the proportion of coloured light of a single wavelength. As saturation increases, so does our perception of the vividness of a colour. (Bottom) Brightness refers to the amplitude of a colour.

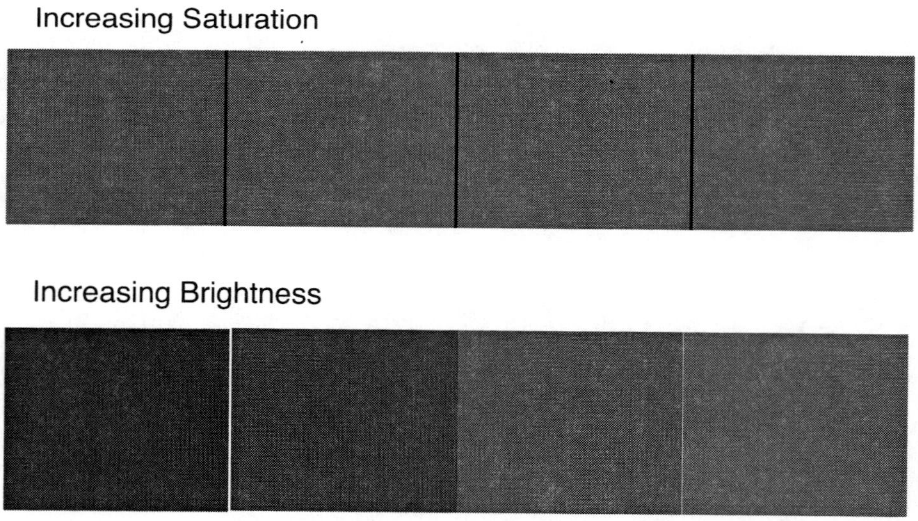

Increasing Saturation

Increasing Brightness

Figure 3

The Eye

The structure and function of the non-retinal parts of the eye were intended for one purpose; to keep a focused and clear image of the outside world projected onto the retina. Understanding how the eye accomplishes this feat begins with a look at the features of the eye.

Parts of the eye

The external layer of the eye is formed by the sclera and cornea. The sclera is commonly known as the 'white' of the eye and is a tough opaque fibrous outer sheath that protects the eye. Although the cornea is made from the same fibers, it is a transparent part of the external layer that allows light to pass through it. To focus the projection of light on to the retina, the eye must progressively bend light (refraction) until it reaches a specific point on the retina. To do so, light is refracted when it travels from one medium to another denser medium. As light passes through the elements of the eye, each element has a particular refractive index that bends light. The cornea accounts for about 80% of all of focusing power of the eye.

The donut shaped iris sits behind the cornea and controls the diameter of the pupils and the amount of light that enters into the eye. The iris is easily recognized because it gives the eye its 'colour'.

Behind the iris is the lens. It is a curved and flexible structure that is responsible for almost all of the remaining 20% of the eye's focusing ability. But the lens is not a static structure like the cornea and is able to change shape to adjust for stimuli that are located at different distances. To bring an image into focus, the lens adjusts itself through the process of accommodation, whereby contracting or relaxing muscles around the lens can change the curvature of the lens, and allow for finely focused light to reach the retina.

When the muscles around the lens are relaxed, the lens becomes flattened resulting in the maximum focal length for viewing objects that are far away. When the muscles around the lens are contracted, the lens becomes rounder and is able to focus objects at close distances onto the retina. The goal of this process is straightforward; all of the elements of the eye function to project a focused pattern of light onto the back of the eye, the retina.

But the lens can only bend light so much. If there is a refractive error at some point during the process of collecting light, the light rays may be focused in front or behind the retina. As a result, the light reaching the retina may actually be out of focus. We commonly refer to refractive errors as based on the nature of the deficit, i.e. nearsightedness and farsightedness.

Draft

Hyperopia (farsightedness). In this condition, individuals report being able to see objects that are far away, but objects that are close appear blurry. This is due to the fact that the lens does not have enough curvature to bend light, such that the image that falls on the retina is blurred.

Myopia (nearsightedness). In this condition, individuals report having clear vision for near objects, but objects that are further away appear blurry. In this case, the light is focused in front of the retina.

Failure to focus light on the back of the retina can happen because:

1. The length of the eyeball is different from normal. Nearsighted individuals tend to have a slightly longer eye length. Far sighted individuals tend to have a slightly shorter eye length.
2. The curvature of the cornea could be different from normal.
3. The power of the lens (the ability to change shape) may be increased or decreased relative to normal.

Corrective lenses or laser eye surgery can be used to treat the symptoms of refractive error problems. Corrective lenses bend incoming light to adjust for any of the above refractive error so that it is focused directly on the retina.

THE RETINA

Light entering the cornea is projected onto the back of the eye, where it is converted into an electrical signal by a specialized sensory organ, the retina. The retina is a transparent sheet of tissue with multiple layers. The photoreceptors (rods and cones) are found in the outer layers closest to the choroid epithelium. The horizontal, amacrine and bipolar cells form the intermediate layer, and the ganglion cells are found on the internal surface layer. Light must pass through all layers of the retina before reaching the light sensitive photoreceptors. The absorption of light by the photoreceptors stimulates a biochemical message that can be translated into an electrical signal that can then be sent through the retina to the bipolar cells, then the ganglion cells (the ganglion cells form the optic nerve). The horizontal and amacrine cells are primarily responsible for lateral interactions between the connections in the retina.

The photoreceptors

There are two kinds of photoreceptors that can be described based on their shape; rods and cones. These two kinds of receptors are not equally distributed across the retina and they serve different functions in processing visual information. The two types of photoreceptors differ so markedly that the retina is referred to as **a duplex retina** (as in a building that has two different houses under the one roof). In brief, we can summarize a number of important distinctions in the function of rods and cones.

The **rods** contain the visual pigment rhodopsin that is highly sensitive to light and are exclusively active during *scotopic* (low light) vision. A total loss of rods produces only night blindness. **Cones** are responsible for day vision (people who lose functioning in the cones are legally blind). There are three different kinds of cones, each of which is most sensitive to a different wavelength of light. Because of this, cones are referred to as **chromatic** and this allows us to see colour.

Rods and cones also differ in the degree of convergence onto a single target cell. Convergence occurs when more than one neuron synapses onto another neuron (Figure 4). We can appreciate just how much convergence there must by consider that over 125 million photoreceptors (the input of the retina) converge onto only 1 million ganglion cells (the output of the retina). Rods represent over 95% of all the photoreceptors in the retina, suggesting that rods must converge onto ganglion cells more than rods. On average, the input from about 120 rods converges onto a single ganglion cell. The high degree of convergence helps the rod system to be a better light detector because a small response from multiple rods can combine together to generate a greater response to their output cells. However, this convergence reduces the spatial resolution of the rod system. In contrast, the input from about 6 cones converges to a single ganglion cell. As a result, cones are able to maximize the discrimination of fine detail, which is an important aspect of our visual acuity.

Figure 4. Schematic representation of photoreceptor convergence (triangles and cylinders) to output cells. (Left) photoreceptors that connect individually to output cells are capable of conveying information about detail. (Right) Many photoreceptors converging on to a single output cell will lose information about detail, but can add up responses from a number of photoreceptors to be more sensitive to lower levels of light.

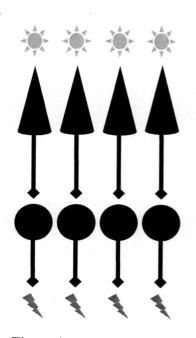

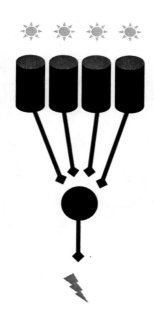

Figure 4.

Distribution of photoreceptors across the retina

The number of rods and cones vary quite markedly across the surface of the retina (Figure 5). For instance, in the very center of our retina (0 deg), we only have cones (see grey plot). There are about 5 million cones across the retina, but the greatest proportion of cones is found in the fovea. The fovea is a specialized area of our retina located directly in line with what you are focusing on. Cones are also present across the remainder of the retina, but in far less numbers. Rods are densely packed across most of the retina. As we look at the distribution of rods, there are a couple of interesting points to note. There are about 20 times more rods than there are cones in the retina (about 120 million rods). However, in the fovea, there are no rods present.

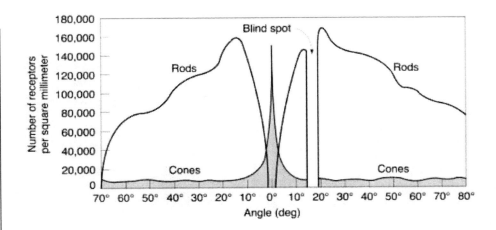

Figure 5. Distribution of rods and cones across the retina. Cones are most concentrated in the fovea. Rods are absent from the fovea and most concentrated in the close periphery (20 deg away from the fovea). No receptors are found at the optic disk, and this area is aptly referred to as the 'blind spot'.

Figure 5.

Response to light

The function of rods and cones is to transduce light into an electrical signal that can be interpreted by the visual system. The outer segments of the receptors contain a stack of discs have photopigment molecules. These molecules have two components: (1) a protein called opsin, and (2) small light sensitive molecule called retinal. The molecule retinal reacts to light and starts a cascade of evens that is known as visual transduction whereby the reaction of one photopigment leads to the activation of about a million other molecules. It is this massive activation that leads to the generation of a response in the receptor. An interesting feature of rods and cones is that they are active in the dark and the absorption of light actually inhibits (hyperpolarizes) the activity of photoreceptors.

Dark adaptation

Our eyes adapt to, and function, over a wide range of light intensities. Just think about the last time you walked across campus on a sunny and then entered into a dimly lit lecture hall. Do you recall how dark it seemed when you first walked in? But that feeling seems to go away after several minutes. We can explain these observations using our understanding of the duplex nature of the retina.

Our adaptation to dark is a multi-step process and reflects the adaptation of both cones and rods (Figure 6). The dark line shows the two stages of the adaptation to light. During the first few minutes of dark exposure, there is an immediate improvement in our sensitivity to light that appears to taper after 3-5 minutes. The initial adaptation reflects changes in the sensitivity of cones. The sensitivity of the rod pathway begins to improve considerably after 5-10 minutes and this change is reflected in the second part of the dark adaptation curve at the point called the rod-cone break. If you've ever wondered why it's so difficult to see colour at low

Draft

luminance levels, it's because only rods are functioning at this time (Rushton, 1961).

The increase in sensitivity of both rods and cones that occurs during dark adaptation is related to visual pigment regeneration. The slow adaptation of the rods compared to the cones happens in part because rod pigment regenerated more slowly than cone pigment.

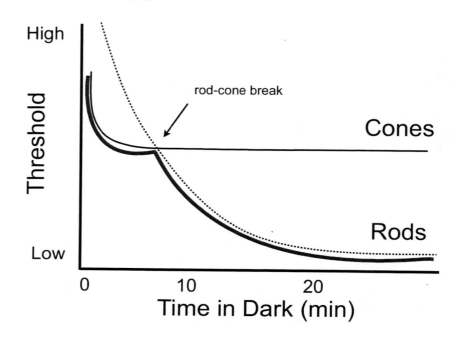

Figure 6. Dark-adaptation curves. The solid black lines show the minimal intensity of light that is needed for a person to see over a given amount of time spent in the dark. The solid line actually represents two separate adaptations, with the cone adaptation representing the first portion of the curve. The second portion of dark adaptation reflects further changes in the sensitivity of rods.

Figure 6

Receptive Field properties of the retina

As light activates photoreceptors, it creates an electrical signal that flows through a network of neurons in the retina before reaching the ganglion cells, which then transmit these signals out of the back of the eye forming the optic nerve. However, the electrical signal is not passively sent through the retina. By the time the neural signals reach the ganglion cells, the response to light is now different. Although light hyperpolarizes photoreceptors, this signal can connect with bipolar cells that either *increase* (turn ON) or *decrease* (turn OFF) activity in response to the photoreceptor signal. The ON and OFF signals of bipolar cells are next sent to retinal ganglion cells.

In 1952, Steven Kuffler demonstrated the receptive field properties of retinal ganglion cells (which is the output of visual information from the eye). The receptive field is defined as the area of the retina that, when stimulated, influences the firing rate of the ganglion cell. He found that when light is presented outside of the receptive field (part A), it doesn't change the firing rate of that neuron. However, stimulating anywhere inside of region B causes the firing rate of that ganglion cell to go up. It was also found that stimulating outside of the central region caused a negative, or opposite response to what was presented in the center. Kuffler's physiological demonstration shows the structure of the retinal ganglion receptive field.

1. It's circular
2. It has a center and an antagonistic surround.

We can explain the organization of center-surround receptive fields by understanding that multiple ON and OFF bipolar cells converge on to a single ganglion cell. The fact that the center and the surround produce opposite responses, we refer to this property as center-surround antagonism. Some cells may also have a center that decreases the firing rate of a ganglion cell and a surround that increases its firing rate. We call these either 'on-center' or 'off-center' depending on the nature of their responses. The center-surround organization of the ganglion cell receptive field can be traced back to the action of horizontal cells across the retina. Horizontal cells are able to laterally inhibit activity in neighboring regions of the retina. This lateral inhibition provides our visual system with the ability to detect differences (or **contrast**) in the visual scene.

Output of the retina

About a 1.5 million retinal ganglion axons form the optic nerve, which run from the back of the eye through the **optic disk** of the retina to the brain. Since there are no photoreceptors in the optic nerve, this region of the retina cannot respond to light. As a result, it is known as the **'blind spot'**. We don't see the blind spot under normal conditions because our other eye can fill in the missing information. But our visual system helps with this process too.

Visual Pathways

RIGHT AND LEFT VISUAL FIELDS

Each eye is able to see a part of visual space: this is its visual field. The visual fields of both eyes overlap extensively to create a binocular visual field. We can describe the visual field as consisting of the right and left hemi-fields that can be further broken down into a binocular zone and two monocular zones. The image projected onto your retina can be cut down the middle, with the fovea defining the center. We refer to the nasal hemi-retina as the half of each retina that is closest to the nose and the temporal hemi-retina as the half of each retina that is closest to the temple.

Images are inverted as they pass through the lens. Therefore, in your right eye, the nasal retina (the half of a retina that is closest to the nose) sees the right half of the world, while the temporal retina (the half of the retina closest to the temple) sees the left half of the world. The right eye's nasal retina and the left eye's temporal retina see pretty much the same thing. In fact, for every object that you can see, usually both eyes are actually seeing it. In fact, Information about the world enters both eyes with a great deal of overlap and this is crucial for depth perception.

The introduction of visual fields is an important concept to understand because the visual system is organized in such a way that keeps visual information from the right half of the visual field separated from the Left half of the visual field. Ultimately, all information from the right half of the environment is represented in the Left half of the brain and all the information from the left half of the environment is represented in the right half of the brain.

PROJECTIONS FROM THE RETINA

Retinal ganglion axons exit the eye through the optic nerve. Visual information from the nasal fields cross at an x-shaped junction of the optic nerve known as the optic chiasm, while visual information from the temporal fields do not cross, but rather continue along the optic nerve on the side from which they originated. This means that visual information from the right half of each retina (the left visual field) travels to the right side of the brain, and visual information from the left half of each retina (right visual field) travels to the left visual cortex. The result of this cross over means that all information from the right half of our environment is processed in the left half of the brain and all information from the left half of our environment is processed in the right half of the brain.

SUBCORTICAL TARGETS

Retinal fibers from both eyes then enter the optic tract, which projects to 4 different subcortical targets. The pretectal area of the mid-brain controls pupilary reflexes in response to changes in brightness. The retinohypothalamic fibers regulate circadian rythms. The superior colliculus controls saccadic (high velocity) eye movements and coordinates visual, auditory and somatosensory information. If I snap my fingers, you could easily turn your head and look in the direction of my hand. It's so automatic that it seems simple. But is it really that easy? Our ability to localize the source of a sound relies on a complex series of neural computation that translate auditory localization into a neural representation of space. Places like the superior colliculus align the auditory and visual maps together. Finally, there is the Lateral Geniculate Nucleus (LGN), the major relay termination of all visual information allowing for conscious visual perception. The LGN does much more than just receive and pass along ganglion signals from the retina to visual cortex though. While as many as 90% of all retinal inputs terminate at the LGN, the LGN also receives signals from the brain stem, the thalamus, and higher centers in the brain. The LGN thus also plays a major role in regulating visual information to primary visual cortex.

The LGN contains six distinct layers of cells. The cells are layered from 1 to 6 and each layer receives input from only one eye and one of two functionally distinct types of retinal ganglion cells. P cells (for parvocellular) have smaller cell bodies and convey detailed information that is useful for the perception of colour, pattern, form, texture and depth. M-cells (for magnocellular) have larger cell bodies and convey information about movement. Layers 1 and 2 receive inputs from the magnocellular ganglion cells and layers 3,4,5,6 receive inputs from the parvocellular ganglion cells. Ganglion cells in the retina send visual information in a highly organized way to points in the lateral geniculate nucleus, so that there is a retinotopic representation of the *contralateral* (meaning opposite) half of the visual field in each LGN.

The LGN has similar receptive field properties as the retinal. Cells in the LGN have a circular center-surround receptive field. The biggest difference is that the receptive fields are a little larger, but not by much.

Organization of Primary visual cortex

In 1902, Korbian Broadmann painstakingly identified as many as 52 distinct regions in the human visual cortex, using architecturally distinct markers in the organization and classification of cells in visual cortex. At the time, he did not have the means to identify the functional role of these regions. However, we now know that his these distinct anatomical areas, like area 17, 18, and 19 (among others) play a very important part in vision and each area performs a very distinct visual function.

Primary visual cortex (area 17 or V1) is the first part of the cerebral cortex that is responsible of processing visual stimuli. What defines primary visual cortex from all other regions of the brain, including other visual areas is a very distinct anatomical marker (named for its discoverer) that runs through V1. This stripe is commonly known as the **line of Gennari**, and because it is such a prominent feature of visual cortex, researchers have come to also call this region of the brain **"the striate cortex"**.

PRIMARY VISUAL CORTEX

Primary visual cortex (V1) has a representation of the contralateral visual hemifield. The inner quadrants (1-4) represent just a couple degrees of visual space. If we look at what parts of the visual cortex are activated by this, there are a few things to note. What presented on the upper half of the activates the bottom half of visual cortex. The central visual field is represented at the posterior pole, whereas the more peripheral regions are mapped in progressively more anterior parts. We can say that the visual cortex maintains a topographic representation of visual space Finally, there is a large magnification of the central few degrees relative to any other region. In fact, the smallest portion of the visual field (the fovea) has the greatest representation in visual cortex when compared to any other part of the visual field.

Primary visual cortex, like every cortical area is actually made up of a thin sheet of grey matter (about 2mm thick). If we look closer at the grey matter, primary visual cortex consists of six layers of cells (layers 1-6) between the surface and the underlying white matter. The principal layer for visual inputs from the optic radiation of the LGN is layer 4. Layer 4 is such a prominent feature that it defines the line of gennari.

There is a lot of information that is being sent to visual cortex, and the visual system has to do a lot of work to keep information about visual space, colour, form, detail, motion, and the left and right eyes together. As a result, the visual system is organized into a number of functional 'modules' that maintain a high level of organization. Let's take a look at the response properties of visual cortex and how this information is organized in visual cortex.

FEATURE DETECTORS IN VISUAL CORTEX

In 1981 David Hubel and Torsten Wiesel received the Nobel Prize for their research describing the organization and physiology of primary visual cortex. Hubel and Wiesel found that many cells in primary visual cortex respond to stimuli much more complex than just spots of light, which are so effective in stimulating retinal ganglion cells in the retina. They discovered that cells in visual cortex respond to features of the visual scene, such as bars of light in a specific orientation (the tilt angle of the bars in a clockwise direction from vertical). Some cells respond to bars of light that are vertical, and thus responses diminish as the bar of light is rotated away from vertical. Cells in visual cortex that respond to the orientation of bars of light are called simple cells. Other neurons, known as complex cells are not only sensitive to the orientation of a bar of light, but also the direction of movement. A hypercomplex cell has all of the features of a complex cell, but is also sensitive to the overall length of the bar of light. Hubel and Wiesel described neurons that respond preferentially to 'features' of a stimulus (such as 'lines', 'motion' and 'edges') as 'Feature Detectors'.

FUNCTIONAL MODULES OF VISUAL CORTEX

Now that we know some of the response properties of visual cortex, let's see how that information is organized. When we describe the organization of primary visual cortex, we often refer to the *columnar* organization. That is, cells that are above below each other tend to share the same properties. In the earliest electrophysiological recordings from visual cortex, it was noticed that whenever two cells were recorded in the same area, they agreed not only in their eye preference, but also in their preferred orientation. In layer 4 of primary visual

114

cortex, inputs from the two eyes remain separate and form alternating *ocular dominance columns*. Similarly, simple cells, with the same orientation preference are grouped together into *orientation columns*. As recordings move across the cortex, ocular dominance alternates eyes and orientation preference varies smoothly from one cell to the next. There are some regions where all orientation converges in radial patterns. These are called Pinwheels (or 'blobs') and define regions that do not have an orientation preference, but do show a preference for other features of a visual stimulus, such as *brightness* and *colour*.

Extra striate cortex

While Hubel and Wiesel's explanation of the receptive field properties were an important contribution to our understanding of the visual system, it doesn't yet explain how objects might be represented. A number of researchers have shown that the visual processing extends beyond primary visual cortex, into the extrastriate areas (which literally means, everything in the cortex that is not the striate cortex). In fact we now estimate that over 30% of the cerebral cortex can be activated by visual stimuli. The extrastriate cortex can be broadly defined into two major streams. Visual information process along the Parietal lobe (or dorsal pathway) processes information about the spatial location of information. Visual information processed along the Temporal lobe (or ventral pathway) is concerned with the identity of objects. This has led researchers to coin these two pathways the 'What' (ventral) and 'Where' (dorsal) streams.

In primates, the extrastriate cortex includes visual areas V2, V3, V4, V5 (sometimes called MT) and IT. Each of these areas has a topographic map of visual space and responds to a different aspect of the visual scene. V2, V4 and IT represent what most vision scientist think of as the 'what' pathway. **Visual area V2** is the second major area in the visual cortex and shares many properties in common with V1. Cells are tuned to simple properties such as orientation, spatial frequency, and color. The responses of many V2 neurons are also modulated by more complex properties, such as the orientation of illusory contours. V4 responds selectively to the colour and simple geometric shaped of a stimulus, like squares and circles. More complex object representations (such as faces) are found in the inferotemporal cortex.

V3 is considered to be part of the dorsal stream, receiving inputs from V2 and from the primary visual area and projecting to the posterior posterior parietal cortex. It has been suggested that area V3 may play a role in the processing of certain kinds of motion, called 'global motion'. Visual area V5, also known as visual area MT (middle temporal), is a region of extrastriate visual cortex that is thought to play a major role in our reported perception of motion

Evolution of the Eye

Think of the many structures of the eye, such as the retina, pupil, lens and cornea working together to capture light in a very precise way. The nature of the eye is so complex that it can be difficult to imagine how the eye could have evolved without a full understanding of natural selection. Charles Darwin described the eye in his book, *On The Origin of Species* under the heading *'Organs of extreme perfection and complication'* and began with the following statement:

> "To suppose that the eye, with all its inimitable contrivances for adjusting the focus to different distances, for admitting different amounts of light, and for the correction of spherical and chromatic aberration, could have been formed by natural selection, seems, I freely confess, absurd in the highest possible degree."

The evolution of the eye has received much consideration and criticisms since Darwin's time. Evolutionary biologists have hypothesized about the precise evolution of the eye by making comparisons with less complex light sensitive (or 'eye-like') structures that exist in species today. These comparisons paint a picture of the development of the precise structure that we call the eye.

Biologists believe that the eye originated from a proto-eye that emerged some 540 million years ago. These very simple proto-eyes were nothing more than light sensitive spots that enabled an organism to tell the difference between light and dark. Since that time, the eye developed into increasing complexity. Some scientists believe some eyes may have evolved in the following way: the simple light-sensitive spot on the skin of some ancestral creature gave it some tiny survival advantage, perhaps allowing it to react to the presence of a predator. If a cluster of spots combined together, they formed a 'patch' of photosensitive cells. Some primitive invertebrates, such as jellyfish, have a 'patch' of photoreceptors that biologists refer to as a 'flat eye'.

Random changes then created a depression in the light-sensitive patch, a deepening pit that made "vision" a little sharper. Lancelets (from the Phylum Chordata) have a curved light sensitive patch that is believed to represent the early formations of an eye cup that allow for the light sensitive patch to provide information about the direction of where light is coming from. Every change had to confer a survival advantage, no matter how slight. If organisms could tell the direction light was coming from, an animal could also sense the direction a predator was coming from.

As the size of the cup gets deeper, our detection of location improves. Even better is a deep eye-cup with a small opening. A small opening begins to allow for precise spots of light to beam on to the retina. In fact, a small opening allows for more detail of the image to be transmitted through (like a pin-hole camera). There is a mollusc (nautulis) that has a pinhole for an eye. It's a relative of the octopus and the eye is defined with only a pinhole opening to the light sensitive patch.

The adaptation to a direction of movement is believed to be closely related to a change in body form: The sensory organs became concentrated at one end of the body, towards the main direction of movement (i.e. the head!).

Now a pinhole camera is not a perfect way of seeing an image. Because it is so narrow, hardly any light can pass through. The answer to this problem is the lens. The close ancestors of the Nautulis, the squid and octopus do have a lens. The lens most likely started as a single transparent sheet across the eye that only served to protect the eye.

Eventually, the light sensitive spot is thought to have evolved into the retina, the layer of cells and pigment at the back of the eye, and the lens is thought to have formed at the front of the eye. It could have arisen as a double-layered transparent tissue containing increasing amounts of liquid that gave it the convex curvature of the human eye.

In our attempt to identify the origins of the eye, it is important to consider that the evolution of the eye is an example of how cumulative selections have given rise to the structure of the eye that we know today. In each step we must identify the benefits that each new eye confers.

Colour and Depth Perception

Colour is important for detecting patterns and objects amongst a background. For example, a red berry stands out against a background of green leaves. Colour vision adds something distinctive and important to simple brightness perception. The perception of colour allows us to distinguish features of objects when borders and contours do not.

The processing of colour begins right in the retina where three cone types respond maximally to three different wavelengths of light: red, green and blue. Because there are three kinds of cones, we say that our colour vision is trichromatic. However, colour perception is not an absolute process. We don't perceive the physical parameters of light in a straightforward manner; it's not simple input to output, or just detecting the wavelength of reflected light. There is a sophisticated *abstracting* process that occurs. We can explore this property through a demonstration of colour constancy.

Colour is a constant property of an object. The surface of the object absorbs some wavelengths and reflects others. The wavelength of the reflected light determines what colour the object is. However, the composition of a wavelength reflected from the object is determined not only by its reflectance, but also by the wavelength composition of the illuminating light. Light from incandescent bulbs is very yellow compared to the blue light of fluorescent light bulbs, or the dull light of a cloudy day. There is a tremendous about of variation in the wavelength of light available across these conditions. But a banana still looks yellow on a cloudy day, a dimly lit room, or under a bright fluorescent bulb. Our colour vision corrects for the variation in the overall illumination so that the object's colour appears about the same. This property of color vision is known as **color constancy**.

Variations of Colour Vision

Colour vision varies across the animal kingdom. Humans are trichromats. So are bees, and macaque monkeys! Bees however, are sensitive to ultraviolet light. Some animals, such as goldfish, pigeons, and ducks have eyes containing four types of retinal receptors. Not animals enjoy trichromatic colour vision. Other animals such as rabbits, cats and squirrels are dichromats; that is, they have only two kinds of cone types. Even further are monochromats, which is any creature that lacks chromatic vision entirely. They must resolve objects by differences in brightness and contrast alone.

Colour Mixing

If you have normal colour vision, you can probably easily match any colour you see by combining lights of the three primary colours: blue, green, and red. There are two ways that we can combine colours together; by mixing lights (**additive**) or pigments (**subtractive**). Additive color mixing is the process of overlapping red, green and blue lights together. The combination of different mixtures of the colour will produce new colours of intermediate wavelength, or if combined all together, will produce a white light. Subtractive colour mixing occurs by combing pigments of colours together, such as paints, or ink. Pigments reflect some wavelengths, but absorb all others (e.g., red paint reflects long wavelengths and absorbs medium and short wavelengths). If all three colours are mixed together each is absorbed, or 'subtracted', and results in the colour black (ink jet printers can produce this effect).

Theories of Colour Vision

Humans can match any colour by mixing light made up of wavelengths of the primary colours: red, green, and blue. The combination of all three primary colours is perceived as white. As a result of these observations, Thomas Young (1802) first proposed that our perception of colour must depend upon the existence of 3 colour receptors and each of which is sensitive to a different wavelength of light. Hermann von Helmholtz added to this theory in the 1850s to propose that there were receptors sensitive to red (long), green (medium) and blue (short) wavelengths of light.

According to the Young-Helmholtz theory of trichromatic colour vision, a short wavelength of light (blue) will strongly activate the short wavelength receptors, but only a weak activation of the other receptors, giving rise to the perception of blue. A yellow light will produce a more a more intermediate response of the medium and short wavelength receptors. Thus, the brain interprets what colour is visible based on the relative strength of the three cone types. In support of the trichromatic theory of colour vision, researchers have been able to identify three different cone visual pigments, each of which is maximally sensitivity to a different wavelength of light.

While the trichromatic theory does a good job of explaining the majority of perceptual phenomena, three important phenomena still remain unexplained. For instance, stare at the coloured squares in Figure 7 for a period of about 1 minute and then move your gaze to the image with white squares. What do you see? Rather than seeing 4 white squares, they appear to be coloured. This is called an afterimage. Notice that the positions of the green/red areas and blue/yellow areas have switched spots! Ewald Hering was the first to describe this visual illusion and he thought that it was very important because it told us something about how perception of colour works. Specifically, this aftereffect cannot be explained by the trichromatic theory of colour perception.

Figure 7. The perception of colour afterimages cannot be explained by the trichromatic theory of colour vision.

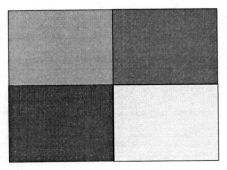 

Figure 7.

Hering also noticed that two colors, side by side, interact with one another and change our perception of them. The effect of this interaction is known as *simultaneous contrast*. If you look at Figure 2, you'll see that the X drawn through the black box appear to be brighter (or more yellow) than the X drawn through the yellow box. While there is nothing different about the two X patterns, we perceive the colour to be different based on the background pattern.

Figure 8.

Finally, Hering also drew attention to the fact that combinations of red, green and blue can usually describe our perception of colour. For instance, you might be able to describe a colour as bluish-green. However, some colour combinations seem to be impossible. No one ever speaks of a greenish-red colour or a yellowy-blue. In fact, we could describe the colours red/green and blue/yellow to be mutually exclusive to one another.

Based on these three observations Hering proposed the **opponent-process theory**. According to Hering, our perception of colour relies on three mutually antagonistic mechanisms that process the information received by cones and recode them into a signal in relation to pairs of colours. These form different colour channels. Similar to the antagonistic center-surround receptive field organization of the retina, these opponent channels would respond in opposing directions to pairs of colours. One set of neurons encodes black-white differences, corresponding to intensity or luminance differences in the field. Another set of neurons responds to red and green color differences and a third set responds to yellow and blue differences. In the retina, we can think of these channel win the perspective of the retinal ganglion cell receptive field organization. For instance, a red-green cell would increase its activity as a result of stimulation with red (R) light and would decrease its activity in response to green (G) light. It can be said to signal +R-G. Other cells signal the opposite; the presence of green and the absence of red (+G-R). A blue-yellow cell would signal +B-Y (some signal +Y-B). Although there is no 'yellow' cone, yellow channels are made up from the response properties of both medium (green) and long (red) wavelength sensitive cones. We perceive colour when there is a relative difference in the activity is biased towards one of the colour cells. We don't see colours like 'reddish-green' because the simultaneous activation of the red cell and the green cells in a +R-G channel because the positive response of red would be canceled out by the negative response of green, yielding no relative difference in the activation of this channel.

We can explain the perception of colour afterimages from our understanding of colour opponent channels. While staring at a red patch, you are stimulating the cells that are coding for the colour red, but not stimulating cells that code for the colour green. The relative difference in activation gives rise to the perception of red. However, during this process the red channel is also depleting its resources, becoming 'fatigued' as a result of prolonged stimulation. When the red patch is removed, the activity of the fatigued red cells are less than normal and even lower than the baseline activity of the opponent green channel. This relative difference in activity between the green and red cells is enough to trick our visual system, giving rise to the perception of green.

So which theory is correct? Well…both! To have a complete understanding of colour perception we need to acknowledge that both theories provide an important contribution to our understanding of colour perception. The Trichromatic theory of colour helps us to understand the functioning of cones in the retina. On the one hand, the opponent process theory helps us to understand the processing of colour from later stages of visual processing, such as the output of the retinal ganglion cells and colour processing in the LGN.

Colour Processing

IN THE RETINA

In the retina, two processing channels stream information to higher visual centers. The low-resolution channel receives input from M-type ganglion cells that tend to have larger receptive fields, are achromatic and conveys information about contrast and movement in the visual field. Alternatively, the high resolution channel receive input from P-type ganglion cells, tend to have smaller receptive fields and is capable of conveying colour information as well as fine detail.

P-type ganglion cells constitute about **80%** of all ganglion cells retina. Two subtypes are defined by the organization of cone inputs. The "red-green" opponent type receives inputs only from long and medium wavelength sensitive cones, whereas the "yellow-blue" type receives input from all three classes of cones.

The spatial organization of the P cell's receptive field and the different cone types allow P-type ganglion cells to convey both **detail** and **colour** information in a complex signal. Let's consider the receptive field properties of a +G-R retinal ganglion cell to see how this is possible.

All ganglion cells in the retina respond to spots of light. When the light is either very small or confined to the center in a way that does not disturb the average level on the surround, only the central part of the receptive field generates a signal. In this case, the retinal ganglion cell becomes active regardless of the stimulating wavelength of light. Stimulation on the surround of the receptive field will decrease activity of the retinal ganglion cell.

Normally, when 'white' light falls on both the center and the surround, it doesn't produce a change in the responsiveness of a retinal ganglion cell. However, the cell will respond well to variations in wavelengths, being excited by some hues and inhibited by others. According to the colour opponent theory of colour vision, our perception of requires some kind of a comparison across different cone types. If a green light is presented over the center and surround of the receptive field, the increase in activity of the green center, relative to the poor response of the red surround trigger the activation of that retinal ganglion cell. Conversely, a red light over the entire receptive field will result in a large negative response of the red surround relative to the poor response of the green center. The relative difference of activation from different wavelengths of light is critical to our perception of colour. So a P cell responds well to brightness variations in the fine structure of an image as shown by a spot of light presented to the center or surround AND it responds well to color variation in the coarse structure of the image as shown by spots of light presented over the entire center and surround.

IN THE LGN

The information provided from the P-type retinal ganglion cell is sent to the parvocellular layers in the LGN. Most Parvocellular cells appear to respond to colour and have a center – surround receptive field organization, just like the retina.

IN PRIMARY VISUAL CORTEX

The response to colour is more complex in primary visual cortex than in the retina and the LGN. When primary visual cortex is stained for and enzyme that is a marker of metabolically active areas, distinct 'blobs' appear in layer 2 of primary visual cortex. Blobs are organized in a very regular fashion, in the middle of the ocular dominance columns. The code the brain uses to convey information about color is charged in the primary visual cortex. In particular, "Blobs" are regions of visual that have a high concentration of "special colour cells" in primary visual cortex. Cells within each CO blobs are sensitive to colour and low frequency spatial information.

Blobs are thought to be the colour area in visual cortex, and their principle output is to a distinct anatomical region of V2 called the "thin-stripes" blobs in V1 project information to the thin stripes of V2, which in turn sends information to V4. Some cells in area V4 respond in a way that does correlate with our perception of colour.

Colour Blindness

Our perception of colour relies on the proper functioning of the cones. Each cone is sensitive to a different wavelength of light and the combined responses from the all of the cones give rise to our perception of colour. Colour Blindness is a term used to describe the lack of sensitivity to certain colours and is the result of a partial or complete loss of function of one or more of the different cone systems.

Many people think that colour-blind people see only in black and white. But this is a common misconception. It is quite rare to be completely colour-blind (monochromatic), but it is much more common to have a more subtle colour vision deficiency. Colour-blind people still see some colour, depending on the degree of the deficit. When comparing colour vision for a trichromat (normal sighted person) and a dichromat (individual with only two functional cone types), we can describe these conditions based on the nature of the cone dysfunction. *Protanopia* refers to the loss of the long wavelength sensitive cone. *Deuteranopia* is the loss of the mediums sensitive cone and *tritanopia* as the loss of the short wavelength sensitive cone. These individuals are still able to perceive some colour, but the range of perceived colours is limited.

PREVALENCE OF COLOUR-BLINDNESS

Nearly 8% of the male population either cannot distinguish red from green or perceive red and green differently from most people. This is the most common form of colour blindness, but interestingly, it affects less than 0.5% of all females. The fact that there is such a difference between males and females suggest that the gene that leads to red-green color blindness is sex-linked and found in the X Chromosome (for which males have only one copy). Typically in females, the stronger chromosome takes precedence so they retain correct vision. The son of a woman carrying a faulty gene has a 50% chance of inheriting the faulty X chromosome and as a result – suffering from color blindness.

Blue and yellow colour vision deficits affect males and females equally as the gene is found on a different chromosome (chromosome 7). The incidence of Tritanopia is quite rare, occurring in fewer than 1 in 10,000 people (or 0.01%). Complete lack of colour perception (achromatopsia) is extremely rare, affecting only 0.00001% of the population.

Depth, Distance & Motion

Depth perception is so automatic that it seems unremarkable. But our perception of depth is nothing short of a miracle when you consider that the image that is projected on to the back of each retina is 2-dimensional. Our visual system must decode the information provided by each eye to give rise to this perception. Our visual system has the difficult task of extracting 3-dimensonal (3-D) information from a 2-dimensonal (2-D) source.

We can get some depth information from monocular depth cues (cues that only need to be seen by one eye), but to achieve stereopsis we require two eyes, and these two eyes must be able to view the same visual field from slightly different positions. To perceive depth and distance, our visual system utilizes a number of binocular cues provided by the coordinated use of both of eyes (binocular cues) as well as cues that are present in the environment (monocular cues).

Binocular cues to depth.

At the end of the 19th century, Charles Wheatsone created the stereoscope, a device that creates the illusion of depth from a two dimensional image. Wheatsone realized that our binocular perception of depth is largely due to the fact that our two eyes see the world from a slightly different perspective. To make his stereoscopes work, he took two photographs of the same scene, but the pictures were taken about 60mm apart from one another (this is about the distance between the center of our eyes). If each of these images is presented to an observer at the same time (from the stereoscope), the observer will perceive the scene as having depth.

For about 50 years, the stereoscope was a common item in every house, sort of like an early television, but these days you find them in antique shops. Of course the effect of viewing images in 3-D is more popular than ever. Movies and television sets are moving towards providing content in 3-D. The process may be more sophisticated than the stereoscope, but the idea is still the same.

We are able to use our two eyes to perceive depth for objects that are up to 30 meters away from us. Within this distance, our visual system is able to compare the differences in the images that are falling on to each retina; slight differences in the horizontal position of the two retinal images leads to binocular disparity. The ability to see depth using only binocular disparity is called stereopsis.

While binocular disparity is a primary binocular cue to depth, it is not the only one. As objects move closer to our face, the gazes of our eyes turn together, changing their angle. Convergence refers to the cues provided by feedback from the extraocular muscles of our eyes during this task.

Draft

MONOCULAR CUES TO DEPTH

Monocular cues to depth are any cues that can be used to estimate distance with information from just one eye. These cues can be broken down into three principle categories: Accommodation, Motion, and Pictorial cues.

ACCOMMODATION

The lens changes shape to focus both near and far objects onto the retina. Accommodation refers to a change in the tension of the muscles surrounding the lens to provide a focused image on the retina.

MOTION CUES TO DEPTH

Motion parallax is a cue to depth base on our own motion. If you are traveling in a car, you can see that objects that are close to you appear to be moving in a blur, while objects in the far distance might be moving much more slowly. This difference in apparent speed of near and far objects is called motion parallax.

Optic flow Optic flow refers to the perceived motion of the visual field that results from an individual's own movement through the environment. As we move through our environment, objects that are closer to us appear to be moving faster than objects that are further away. Optic flow can be easily simulated with dots moving in a correlated fashion

PICTORIAL CUES TO DEPTH

Prior to the 1400's, artists struggled to create a sense of depth in their images. Paintings typically varied the size of objects to give them a sense of importance, rather than a sense of depth. The only consistently used method to convey a sense of depth was by overlapping objects in a painting. If one object overlaps and thereby occludes another object, we perceive it to be closer to us. This is known as **interposition**.

Near the end of the 15th century, artists began to make use of a mathematical perspective on art to create a vivid sense of depth. Many artists realized that because objects appear to shrink and parallel lines come together with the distance, that this ought to be conveyed in their art if they desired it to better represent our everyday perceptions. Parallel lines will appear to converge on a single vanishing point in the horizon, called the one-point perspective, or **linear perspective** cues to depth.

AERIAL PERSPECTIVE

Leonardo da Vinci has been credited as one of the first artists to describe and use the atmosphere and its effect on the colour of distant objects to create a sense of depth. He even went so far as to suggest rules for applying these effects to create a

Draft

sense of depth in his images: "Thus if one is to be five times as distant, make it five times bluer." Before da Vinci's time, more distant objects were drawn or painted higher on the picture plane, and sometimes smaller, but with no less detail or color saturation. Leonardo was the first to make careful measurements and call the subject aerial perspective. Aerial perspective is the visual effect of light when passing through an atmosphere. Specifically, the scatter of light in the atmosphere causes very distant objects to appear hazy and bluer.

Our expectations also play a strong role in our sense of **depth from shading**. Our experience tells us that light will come from above us (Figure 3). As a result, our sense of depth is firmly linked to our understanding that light comes from above and how shadows should be cast. When the shaded area is presented on the bottom, we perceive a strong sense that the circle is popping out at us and sunk into the page when the shaded area is on the top.

Figure 3. Depth from shading. The gradient of shading on the circles gives a strong sense of depth.

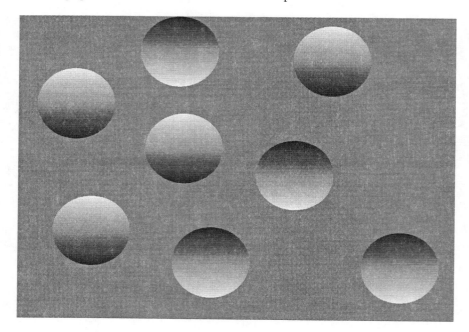

Figure 9.

Development of Depth Perception

Researchers have often wondered whether depth perception is innate or learned. Research has demonstrated that it is both. An infant's ability to perceive depth requires the use of stereopsis as a binocular cue to depth or some knowledge of the environment to interpret monocular cues to depth. At birth, binocular cues are of little use, because infants can't coordinate eye movements and are not be able to do so reliably until 3 months of age.

By 4 months of age, infants are able show a distinct reaching preference for objects that are closer to them (Granrud, Yonas, and Pettersen, 1984). Around the time that infants start to crawl, most distinguish deep and shallow surfaces and avoid dangerous-looking drop-offs. This has been studied using an apparatus called a visual cliff, a box with a glass platform that extends over a drop of several feet. A checkered pattern just underneath the glass made it seem as though the infant was on a stable floor. However, in the middle of the glass platform, the pattern dropped down several feet, giving the perception of a 'cliff'. In an experiment, an adult (usually the mother) stands on one side of the glass and calls to the child, who is on the other. Gibson and Walk (1960) found that most infants around 6 to 14 months could not be coaxed to crawl over the edge of the "cliff." Such a response indicates that depth perception is present at this age.

Monocular depth perception, using cues such as changes in texture and overlapping objects, develops around the 6 months of age. Many of these cues to depth must be learned in infancy.

The acquisition of binocular skills may be the result of learning or simply due to maturation, but some basic depth capabilities exists at birth. Animal studies using the visual cliff procedure have shown that chicks less than 24 hours old avoid areas where the floor is recessed (Morrison PR. 1982.) Other studies have shown that even animals raised in visually deprived environments that lack normal monocular depth cues avoid the deep side of the visual cliff (Kaufman LW. 1976). Together, these findings make a strong argument that our binocular perception of depth is innate.

Evolution of Depth Perception

Stereoscopic vision is essential for predator animals that catch other animals (owls for example), but has secondary importance for animals that are chased (such as rabbits or deer). As such, ethologists have noticed consistent differences between predators and prey.

Having both eyes at the front of the head allows for the greatest degree of binocular overlap, allowing a predator to accurately locate and capture prey. However, it's not always ideal to have a high degree of overlap because it reduces to total area that can be seen and could allow some visual objects to go undetected. As such, prey animals prefer a panorama view of the world, where their eyes are placed on each side of the head, in some cases allowing a nearly 360 degree field of view. The advantage is that a prey animal is more likely to survive if they can spot the predator. It's almost like they have eyes in the back of their head!

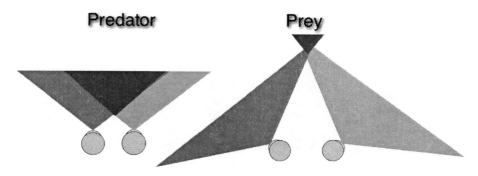

The degree of binocular overlap is substantially greater in predators than prey

Figure 4. The degree of binocular overlap is substantially grater in predators than in prey.

Figure 10

Vision & Eye Development

Measuring infant visual acuity

The most common technique to measure grating acuity is the preferential looking paradigm. This process takes advantage of the fact that newborns prefer to look at patterns over something plain (Fantz et al., 1962). Experimenters will present an infant with two acuity cards, one that is plain grey, and another that has stripes. If an infant can perceive the stripes, they will look at that card preferentially. If the stripes are too fine to be resolved by the visual system, they will not show a preference towards either card. Adults use a similar process except that an adult can verbally indicate where they can see the stripes.

Visual abilities can also be resolved using EEG methods of recording activity during the presentation of visual stimuli, or Visually evoked Potential. The principle of using EEG is simple; if a subject is able to see the object, researchers should be able to record an electrical event in the brain. While visually evoked potentials represent a gold standard in measuring visual abilities, it is usually not a practical approach to employ on infants as it is a time consuming process that require many trials (in the thousands) and functions best when the observer is still.

THE DEVELOPMENT OF VISION

Newborns have all the eye necessary elements to see, but the structures of the eye have not yet fully matured and the organization of the visual system is not yet matured. In fact, of all of the perceptual systems, our visual system is the least developed sense at birth. Both time and visual experience is necessary to drive the maturation of the visual system. We have learned much about the development of sight during different time periods in development.

Draft

PRENATAL PERIOD

There is evidence to suggest that a fetus is sensitive to light as measured by changes in fetal heart rate in the presence of a light stimulus. Premature infants also show the ability track and to focus on objects that are less than a foot away.

NEWBORN PERIOD

Newborns have a lot of visual development to go, but they still display a vast array of visual abilities. Full-term newborns have visual acuity of roughly that is roughly 30 times worse than adults. The preferential looking paradigm to measuring vision has allowed researchers to understand much of what we know an infant can see. Infants show a preference to a variety of stimuli within minutes of birth (such as shapes and faces within minutes of birth). According to some measures, newborn visual acuity is limited to 20/200 to 20/600, meaning that an infant's vision is capable of seeing objects at 20 feet compared to an adult that can see the same object at 200 to 600 feet (Haith, 1991). Despite the lack of detail, a two day old infant is attracted to visual forms and do show a preference to look at faces (Fantz 1961). At two weeks of age, newborns do show some ability to distinguish between opposing colours, such as green and red and are also attracted to moving objects more so than stationary ones. By 3 months of age, Infants develop the ability to track and follow a slow moving. At 6 months, the average visual acuity of infants is 20/80 (Mayer and Dobson, 1980) and the improvement in vision can be directly attributed to the maturation of photoreceptors in the eye (Banks & Bennett, 1988).

EARLY CHILDHOOD TO LATE ADOLESCENCE

Between 8 months and 6 years of age, visual acuity continues to improve to normal adult levels (20/20), but at a much slower rate (Maurer and Lewis, 2001). This prolonged development of visual acuity is believed to reflect cortical development. Around 3-5 years of age children presented with moving point-light are able to form dots together to see configurations depicting a walking person or four-legged animals (called biological motion; Pavlova et al., 2001).

While young children seem to perform well on a number of perceptual tasks, psychologists have found limitations in what they are able to see at this point. In particular, a child's visual system is very sensitive to the quality a stimulus. If researchers degrade the quality of a stimulus by even a small amount (this is called 'adding noise'), children often perform much worse than adults (e.g. Freire et al. 2006). There is even evidence to suggest that children as old as 11 year olds are still affected by noise and adult performance is not reached until 15 years (Schrauf, 1999, Jeon et al., 2010). One possible explanation of the difference in visual function of children might be that the 'higher' visual centers in the extrastirate cortex may not be fully mature until late adolescence, thereby limiting visual function.

Specialized Visual Systems

Not all animals see the world as humans do. For many animals, the world is seen in fuzzy shades of gray. However, other animals can see in total darkness, or even see colors beyond the human visual spectrum. Some animals can even use binocular vision to spot prey from thousands of feet away. There appears to be a tremendous amount of variance of visual abilities to meet the need of animals based on their natural habitat. In this section, we will discuss some of those differences.

Simple eye vs. compound eye

Simple eyes are those that have a single lens. Human eyes are classified as 'simple' because only a single lens collects and focuses light to the retina. In contrast, compound eyes consist of many light and colour sensing elements and are commonly found in arthropods, including many insects and crustaceans. A compound eye consists of hundreds, even thousands of tiny light capturing elements, known as ommatidia. Each ommatidium has its own lens and receptors. Contrary to popular belief, insects do not see hundreds of copies of the same image at once. Rather, each lens makes up a small part of the overall picture, similar to a jigsaw puzzle. Some insect compound eyes (e.g., dragonflies) have upwards of 30,000 ommatidia that are excellent at detecting motion and are able to give a 360-degree view of the environment. However, compared with a simple eye, compound eyes provide very poor information about detail.

Shape of pupil varies across species

Human eyes have circular pupils, but a number of other animals have slit-shaped ones. The orientation of the slits in some animals can be vertical (i.e., crocodiles, snakes, cats, and foxes) or horizontal (i.e., hippopotamuses and sheep) or have vertically oriented slits. A common misconception is that the slit eye better serves nocturnal animals by allowing for a greater pupil diameter at night, thereby allowing for more light to enter the eye. However, this appears not to be the case as round pupils are better at doing so. Rather, it has been found that a slit pupil actually enhances visual acuity as well as increasing the range of intensities over which the eye can function effectively (Malmström & Kroger, 2006). It's believed that the slit pupil reduces chromatic aberration, a tendency for some wavelength of light entering at the periphery to blur the image on the retina.

Size of eyes across species

In general, ethologists find that in virtually all vertebrate animals, anatomical features change proportionally to body size. For instance, brain size is proportional to body size in most animal species. However, biologists have failed to find a similar rule to describe the change in eye size. Rather, eye size seems to vary by utility or function. Birds of prey, such as owls for example, have relatively large eyes because of the importance of hunting and foraging for owl species and the use of large eyes in such contexts. Conversely, underground animals, such as the shrew, tend to have very small eyes relative to their body because they spend most of their time underground. As well, primates have larger eyes than would be predicted by body size, and rodents have smaller ones (Howard et al. 2004).

Different photoreceptors in different species

Look around the room you are in. You probably think you see the world pretty clearly. It is hard for us to imagine an animal seeing better than we do. But, many do. Raptors, or birds of prey, including eagles, hawks, and falcons can see up to 8 times clearer than the sharpest human eye. A golden eagle for example can see a hare from a mile away. The reason for their remarkable vision is related to their flying and feeding habits.

The eagle has eyes that are different to humans, as their retinas are larger and flatter, and thus provide heightened visual acuity. In the center of the eagle's fovea - the focusing point of the retina - there are approximately 1,000,000 cones per mm, compared to 200,000 for humans, thus objects or prey can be seen much more clear and sharp, even at great distances.

In birds that need accurate distance vision the most, (i.e. birds of prey), a second fovea can be found in the lateral part of the retina where the concentration of rods and cones is the highest and therefore vision is the sharpest. Raptors, with their wide binocular field of view, have both a central and lateral fovea. As a result, a substantial proportion of their visual field projects on the most visually receptive parts of the retina.

Motion

Motion is a very primitive function and is present in most animals. It's easy to think of motion perception as being simple; an object moves across our retina and our visual system integrates that information together to form the perception of motion.

But the reality is that our eyes are not static sensory organs. The eyes are constantly moving, and as a result, objects are constantly changing position on the retina. Yet we don't make mistake of perceiving this change of position as movement. Our perception of motion relies on a complex integration of movement on the retina, and feedback on the action of the inter-ocular muscles. In lower animals, such a frogs, sight is limited to motion. Our sight in the very periphery is also limited to motion. At the very extreme, we don't even detect motion, but motion triggers an orienting reflex that tends to bring the moving object into central vision.

Neural Pathways of Motion Perception

Retinal ganglion M-cells don't respond directly to 'motion' but instead respond best to stimuli that change in contrast over time, which is exactly what a stimulus moving across a receptive field would do. In the cortex, the response to motion becomes more specific. Most neurons in primary visual cortex prefer motion in a particular direction, although a subset will respond to movement in any direction. Beyond primary visual cortex, populations of neurons in V2, V3 and even beyond that have strongly preferred directions and are also sensitive to velocity. However, our perception of motion, that is, what we report actually seeing is highly correlated with activity in cells found in extrastriate area V5 (otherwise known as MT). Vision scientists refer to the cells in V5 as 'real motion' cells.

MT is organized in direction columns. Most cells within a single column prefer motion in a particular direction. Neurons are organized in such a way that the adjacent columns contain cells that prefer motion in the opposite direction (DeAngelis and Newsome, 1999).

We can play a trick on area MT to demonstrate the specificity and competition between neurons that prefer motion in the opposite direction. After staring at the motion of a waterfall for about a minute, stop the movement. The after-effect is that the lines on the waterfall appear to be moving up! But in fact they are not. This motion after-effect can be explained by the fatiguing of neurons that signal motion in one direct. This is the same as the concept that we demonstrated in the colour after effect. In the motion after effect example, when the movement stops, the lines of the waterfall appear to be moving upwards because the adjacent neurons in MT are not fatigued and this difference in baseline activity is perceived as motion.

Motion Agnosia

Case studies of motion agnosia reveal the specificity of area MT in our perception of motion. A patient known as L.M. had bilateral damage to area MT. She could see very well in terms of form and colour, but had lost the ability to perceive motion. She would describe life as a series of 'freeze-frame' images. She couldn't cross the street because she couldn't judge the speed of oncoming traffic or pour water into a glass because she couldn't tell how quickly the cup was filing up. She could perceive some movement if it was very slow, but it still appeared to be episodic shifts in space, not real perception of motion.

Draft

Form Perception

Gestalt Principles of Grouping

Do you see the Dalmatian in the picture below? Most of us can relatively easily. But look more closely at the image. Do you see any lines that truly define the dog? In the absence of absolute visual information, our brain actively interprets what we are looking at by seeking out patterns in the environment.

Figure 1. Do you see the Dalmatian? Can you see any lines that define the dog?

Figure 11

Gestalt psychology describes a theory to account for how we perceive the environment. The word "gestalt" roughly translates from German to describe the way something is "put together" or "configured". Gestalt psychology is based on the observation that we often report seeing more than just the sensory information that is falling on our retina. Rather, our visual system puts information together in a way that makes it easier to interpret.

Draft

According to Gestalt psychologists, we attempt to organize visual information into simple groups. For example, if you see one dot, you perceive a singe dot. However, if you see 10 dots side by side, you might report seeing a 'line of dots' (Figure 2). Notice here that we don't report seeing '10 dots', instead rather we group the information together to form some unified perception of a whole (in this case, a line). This organization is captured by a well-known phrase coined by the Gestalt psychologists: "the whole is greater than the sum of its parts".

Figure 12. 10 separate dots or a line of dots?

Gestalt psychologists argue that the visual system is predisposed to draw meaning from the organization of parts of visual stimuli. This later became the **law of Pragnanz**, which states that we have a bias to organize things into the simplest organization. A 'line of dots' is a more simple organization than 'dot, dot, dot, dot, dot, dot, dot, dot, dot, dot'".

Six principles of Gestalt organization

Gestalt psychologists have identified several rules of how our visual system perceptually organizes information.

1. FIGURE-GROUND

When perceiving a visual scene, we organize the information as the central object of identification (figure), while other objects fade into the background (ground). In other words, an object will be perceived as separate from its background.

2. PROXIMITY

Things that are closer together will be perceived as being members of the same group. For instance the pattern below looks like nine separate squares. However, if they are grouped together, we perceive this as a single group (Figure 3).

Draft

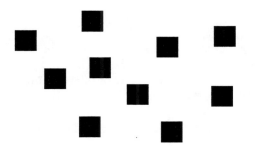

Figure 13. Proximity

3. CLOSURE

Our brains do more than just process information from the visual scene – it actively interprets it! When we see an incomplete object, we tend to fill in the gaps in a process called 'closure' Notice that although the form of the panda is incomplete in the Figure 4, enough information is present for the visual system to fill in the gaps, helping us to form the representation of a panda.

Figure 14. Closure

Draft

4. SIMILARITY

The principle of similarity states that things which share visual characteristics such as shape, size, color, texture, value or orientation will be seen as belonging together. In the example below the shape of the structures gives our visual system the impression that the squares form a '+' sign, even though all objects are organized uniformly across the grid.

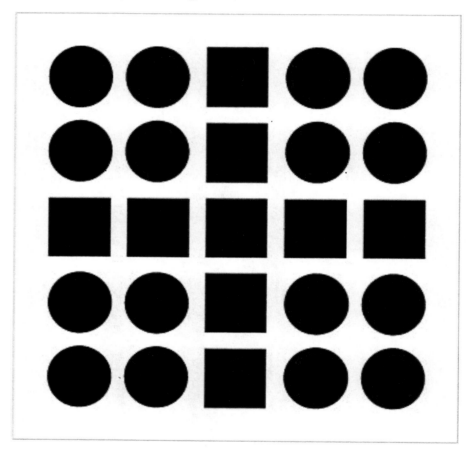

Figure 15. Similarity

Draft

5. CONTINUITY

The law of continuity holds that points that are connected by straight or curving lines are seen in a way that follows the smoothest path. Rather than seeing separate lines and angles, lines are seen as belonging together (Figure 6).

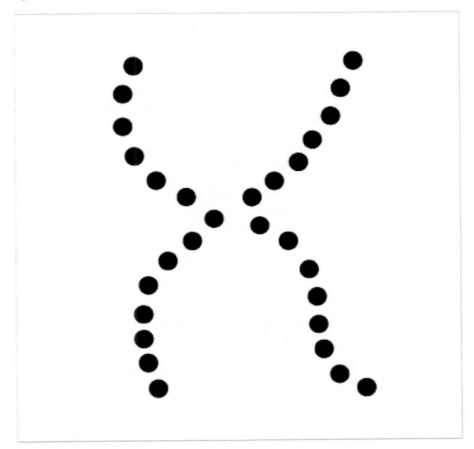

Figure 16. Continuity

6. COMMON FATE

The common fate principle states that elements tend to be perceived as grouped together if they move together. For example, if you are walking outside in the park and there was a green snake lying in the grass, you would probably not notice it. But should that snake begin to move, you would notice it immediately because its movement causes your visual system to organize the figure against the background.

Role of expectation in perception of patterns and objects

The gestalt principles of perceptual grouping illustrate that what we see is a product of more than just the stimulus that falls on our retina, vision is also the result of our expectations of what stimuli should be. When our interpretation emerges from the data (the information provided by the retina), this is known as data-driven, or bottom-up processing. However, when our perception is influenced by sources beyond the images on the retina, such as knowledge or experience, higher-level cognitive processing is engaged to interpret the image. This is known as prediction processing or top-down processing.

The influence of top-down processing has been shown through what is known as the Rat/Man stimulus. Subjects saw this picture after viewing earlier slides that showed line drawings of either animals or faces. Depending on whether they saw animals or faces in previous slides, subjects reported seeing either a rat or a man wearing glasses (respectively). That is, they had been primed for one or the other interpretation of the ambiguous picture by the general information present in the preceding slides. This is a form of top-down processing, where our expectations influence what we perceive.

Draft

Figure 17. Do you see a rat or a man? Our prior expectations influence what we report seeing.

Theories of object recognition in Humans

The study of object recognition is focused on addressing a two-fold question. First, how are objects represented in the brain? Secondly, how do we match unlimited combinations of possible viewing conditions with our representation of each object? Unfortunately, objects are not conveniently labeled for us. Many objects look extremely similar (think about the wide variety of cars and four legged creatures) and most do not even contain a single feature that uniquely identifies them. Any complete theory of how visual objects are recognized must explain how humans are able to reliably identify specific objects from an unlimited number of orientations. In this section we are going to consider theories that describe how the brain organizes object representations and what the brain must do to recognize objects.

Recognition-by-components

Recognition-by-components (Biederman, 1987) is a theory of object recognition that accounts for the successful identification of objects despite changes in the size or orientation of the image. Moreover, recognition-by-components explains how moderately occluded or degraded images, as well as novel examples of objects, are successfully recognized by the visual system.

The Recognition-by-Components (RBC) theory is based on the assumption that just about any object can be represented as an arrangement of 3 dimensional shapes (like cylinder, pyramids, cubes, wedges… etc.) called geons. Geons are apart of an object 'alphabet' and unique combinations of geons form the equivalent of object 'words' that can be readily interpreted by the visual system. As we view an object, our visual system segments the different geons and their relationship to one another. Recognizing a geon involves recognizing the features that define it (feature analysis). Having identified the pieces out of which the object is composed and their configuration, one recognizes the object as the pattern composed from these pieces (a prototype comparison) (Figure 8). A major strength of the RBC theory is that people can typically recognize about 30,000 objects with the use of only 36 different geons. The RBC model argues that we can see objects from an unlimited possible viewpoint in the following because different views of the same object should still lead to the same set of geon recognition. Therefore, the model achieves view invariance.

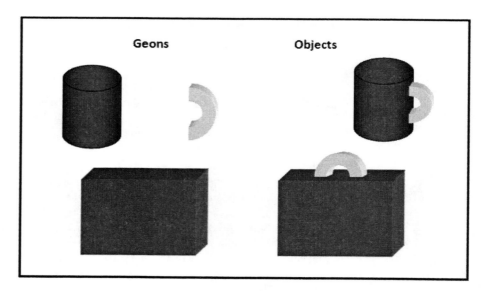

Figure 18. Object recognition using simple geometric shapes called geons.

However, the RBC model does have drawbacks. In particular, Invariant features are difficult to extract in real images. For example, slight variations in the lighting of a room can completely change the unique features of a face that are used for individual identification.

Geons are also poor at representing many natural objects, which may or may not have simple parts-based descriptions. For example, many birds have tapered beaks and could be described by the same geon. However, there is a tremendous amount of subtle variation in the features of a beak from one bird to the next. Our knowledge of geons does not help us to understand how we distinguish between two birds with slightly different features.

Template Matching Model

The Template Matching theory (or model) is another attempt to account for our perception of objects. Incoming sensory information is compared directly to copies (templates) stored in long-term memory. These copies are stored in the process of our past experiences and learning. The Template Match model assumes that a retinal image of an object is faithfully transmitted to the brain and that an attempt is made to compare it compare a stimulus to a large number of literal copies (templates) that are stored in memory in order to find a match against all templates.

This model works well when exact matches are expected (for example, computers search for exact sequences of code to avoid making mistakes. Bar-code readers are an excellent example of this as well). However, this does not work well with

Draft

humans. The template model assumes that our recognition of objects requires a separate 'template' representation for each possible stimulus in every possible position, orientation and size. This would require an extraordinary number of templates to recognize a single object. The Template theory cannot account for how we recognize imperfect matches either. Moreover it cannot account for how the brain would add more templates to memory since an object would not be recognized if it does not make a perfect match with an already existing template. Finally, the template theory does not allow for any alternate interpretations of the perception of the object within the context it is presented in (Figure 9).

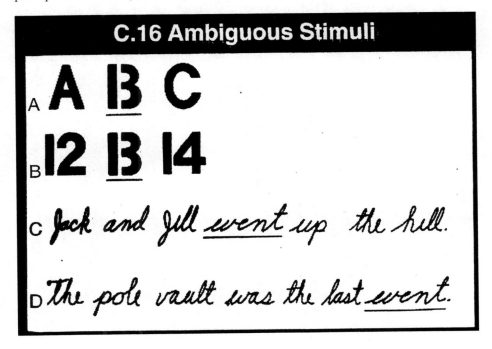

Figure 9. Ambiguous stimuli may be interpreted differently based on their context. This does not fit well with the template theory of object recognition.

Figure 19.

Prototype Model

The Prototype model is a more flexible alternative version of Template model. Instead of storing many fixed representations of a single template, our brain stores prototypes, which are the common characteristics of each object. The perceived object does not need to exactly match the prototype for object recognition to occur, so long as there is a 'family resemblance' to the prototype. There is good evidence that people do form prototypes after exposure to a series of related stimuli. For instance, in a study where subjects were shown a series of patterns that were related to a prototype, but not the prototype itself. When later shown a series of distracter patterns plus the prototype, the participants identified the

Draft

prototype as a pattern they had seen previously (Solso and McCarthy, 1981). This suggests that we are forming a 'prototype' based on our previous experiences.

Perceptual Constancy

So far, we have describe a few different approaches to how the brain organizes object representations and what the brain must do to recognize objects. However, the visual system also has another role to play in interpreting visual stimuli -- perceptual constancy. **Perceptual constancy** describes the tendency of animals and humans to see familiar objects as having standard shape, size, colour, or location regardless of changes in the angle of perspective, distance, or lighting. The impression tends to conform to the object as it is or is assumed to be, rather than to the actual stimulus. For instance, we see the door in Figure 10 to be rectangular in all images, despite the fact that only the image of the door on the left hand side may actually be so.

Figure 10. Perceptual constancy. A door appears to be rectangular despite the fact that the image falling on our retina is often not rectangular.

Figure 20.

The 5 perceptual constancies

1. Shape constancy. This term refers to the tendency to create a fixed representation of the shape of an object, even if there are differences in the viewing angle. This describes the door example in Figure 21.

2. Location (position) constancy. We do not perceive the objects to have changed position despite the fact that our location relative to an object changes as we move through the environment.

3. Size constancy. We are biased to perceive the relative size of a familiar object based on our interpretation of their distance.

4. Brightness constancy. The tendency for a visual object to be perceived as having the same brightness under a wide variety of viewing conditions (Figure 21)

> **Figure 11**. We perceive square A to be darker than square B because of brightness constancy, which accounts for differences in illumination of the visual scene due the shadow cast by the cylinder. However, you can see on the left that if we isolate square A and B from the scene we can see that their true brightness is actually the same

Figure 21.

5. Colour constancy. This term refers to the tendency for a colour to look the same under a wide range of illumination.

Draft

Development of Pattern, Object and Face Recognition

Our sense of sight is enabled with a number of mechanisms that allow us to quickly recognize and process information about motion, depth, colour, patterns and even stimuli as complex as faces. We have already seen that our visual system undergoes a number of functional and perceptual changes over the first years of life. In this section, we will see if the same principles hold true for object perception.

From a historical perspective, psychologists in the 19th century believed that infants are born 'tabula rasa' (blank slate), without any capabilities to recognize objects, and can understand very little of the sensory stimuli that they receive. We now know that this is not entirely true. Researchers have shown that newborn infants do show a preference for some stimuli but many perceptual abilities do not fully mature until much later in childhood.

Object recognition

The environment is filled with objects. We can discern between objects using a number of visual cues such as edges, contours, textures, luminance and colour. Our visual system must extract these features and organize them into groups before giving rise to the perception of a complete object that stands distinctly from its background. Confusing visual cues can complicate this task. For instance, objects may be partly occluded (blocked) by separate overlapping elements, making it more difficult to accurately identify what an object is, or even tell if they are a part of the same object.

By 3 to 4 months of age, infants are able to recognize similar objects and can even discriminate between different categories, such as 'dog' or 'cat (Johnson and Aslin, 1996). Infants as young as 10 months old still lack some of the ability to distinguish between objects, even if one is moving and the other is not. However, at 4 months of age, infants seem to be unable to process visual information using gestalt-like principles.

Size Constancy

The size of an image that is projected on to the retina depends on the distance that the object is away from the retina. Despite large changes in retinal size, our perception of the size of the object remains stable. Carl Granrud (1996) has found that infants as young as 4 months of age are able to distinguish between small objects that are close to them and large objects that are far away.

Face Recognition

Of all the perceptual abilities adults share, our ability to instantly and seamlessly recognize a specific individual from a brief glance is one of the most impressive feats of our visual system. While there is a lot of evidence to suggest that adults are able to improve their perceptual discrimination of faces with practice, the question still remains: are we born with an innate preference for faces or is face recognition and expertise learned during the early infancy? The only way to determine the genetic contribution of face perception is to study whether or not babies show any preference to faces. If they can see faces, can they also recognize specific individuals? Researchers have shown that within minutes after birth, newborns do show a preference to look at face-like stimuli, more so than similar shapes with scrambled face elements (like a nose on the forehead and eyes placed on top of one another; Figure 12) (Goren et al., 1975; Johnson et al., 1991). 1-3 day olds prefer upright faces to inverted ones. Within 4 days, a newborn can recognize their mother from other similar looking faces. These newborn behaviours strongly suggest that the ability to perceive faces is present at birth, supporting the idea that there is an innate preference for faces (Easterbrook et al., 1999). This recognition is thought to be an important element for infant-to-mother bonding.

Figure 12. Simple face stimuli used to demonstrate an infant's preference to look at face like stimuli minutes after birth

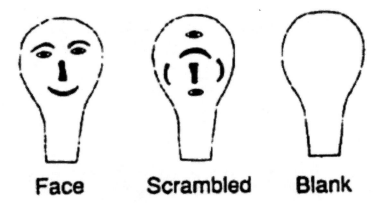

Figure 12.

Visual Illusions

Visual illusions are fascinating to vision scientists. Not only is the effect of a visual illusion entertaining, but it is also tells us something important about how our visual system works and gives meaning to visual input.

The Müller-Lyer illusion

The Müller-Lyer illusion is the observation that we misrepresent the length of an object based on secondary cues given in the image. For instance, the arrow in the middle divides a continuous line in Figure 13 (top). But is the left half longer than the right half? Most would agree that the left side is longer than the right. However, this is not so. If we add a ruler to the image, you'll notice that the arrow in the middle dissects the line exactly in half.

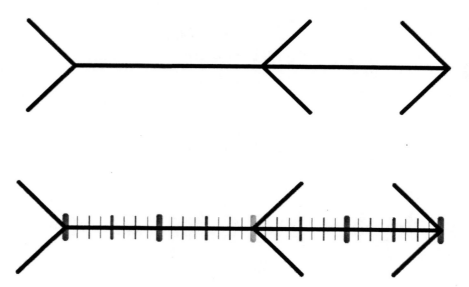

Figure 13. Müller-Lyer illusion

We can understand the Müller-Lyer illusion as a product of top-down processing. The direction of an arrow triggers our familiar cues to depth. When the arrows point outwards, our visual system assumes this edge to be closer to us than a line when the arrows point inwards. According to this theory, our experience of living in a world of human made objects (e.g., buildings and furniture) with right angles drives this perceptual effect. This has come to be known as the 'carpentered world' hypothesis. Interestingly, individuals from more rural areas (and less experience with buildings with right angles) are less susceptible to this illusion.

The Ponzo illusion

If convergence is a cue to depth, we expect lines to get smaller as they recede into the distance. In figure 14, the two yellow lines above are exactly the same size, but they don't appear that way. Our perception is that the yellow line is more distant than the yellow line at the bottom. Take notice of the visual cues in this image. The train tracks are assumed to be parallel to one another. The yellow bar on the top extents past the width of the train tracks, while the yellow bar on the bottom does not. With this evidence in hand, our visual system interprets the line on top as being wider than the line on the bottom even though they are exactly the same length.

Figure 14. Although the two yellow lines are of equal length, our cue to depth (convergence) gives rise to the perception that the line on the top is longer.

Figure 14.

The Matrix Problem

I'd like to end by bringing back two questions I asked at the beginning of this chapter (Do our senses actually give us an accurate picture of the world around us? To what extent can we rely on them to tell us what is really going on 'out there'?) and then ask you several more questions. As we have discussed, our perception of the environment is just that, a perception that results from interpretation of data from physical stimuli in the world. But consider: How can you be sure that the world around you is the way you think it is? How can you be sure that the world around you even exists? How can you be certain that you were not in an accident and that only your brain could be saved and is being kept alive by scientists who feed in data that conforms to your perception of the world? Are you sure that live in the 21st century as you assume, or is it possible that your brain is streamed with data that makes you think you are interacting with your present environment?